Edexcel
GCSE MODULAR MATHEMATICS
Examples and Practice

FOUNDATION

Stage 1

1	Integers	1
2	Fractions and decimals	3
3	Percentages and ratio	25
4	Algebra – structure and symbols	32
5	Algebra – coordinates	39
6	Angles and construction	44
7	Quadrilaterals and circles	53
8	Symmetry and transformations	57
9	Scale and conversions	69
10	Handling data – collecting data	76
11	Handling data – representing and interpreting data	81
12	Probability	93
	Examination-style practice paper	102
	Answers	105

Heinemann

Edexcel
Success through qualifications

About this book

This *Examples and Practice* book is designed to help you get the best possible grade in your Edexcel GCSE maths examination. The authors are senior examiners and coursework moderators and have a good understanding of Edexcel's requirements.

Foundation Stage 1 Examples and Practice covers all the topics that will be tested in your Foundation Stage 1 examination. You can use this book to revise in the run up to your exam, or you can use it throughout the course, alongside the *Edexcel GCSE Maths* Foundation core textbook.

References in the contents list for each section of the book tell you when to find the most relevant paragraph of the specification. For example, NA2a refers to Number and Algebra, paragraph 2, section a.

Helping you prepare for your exam

To help you prepare, each topic offers:
- **Key points** to reinforce the key teaching concepts
- **Teaching references** showing you where the relevant material is covered in both the old and new editions of the *Edexcel GCSE Maths* Foundation core textbook. These references show you where to find full explanations of concepts, and additional worked examples e.g.

Teaching reference:
(*pp 47–49, section 3.1, 3.2*) —— The first reference is to the old edition
pp 53–56, section 3.2, 3.3 —— The second reference is to the new edition

Where material is new to the new specification there is no reference to the old edition textbooks.
- **Worked examples** showing you how to tackle a problem and lay out your answer
- **Exercises** with references showing you which exercises in the *Edexcel GCSE Maths* Foundation core textbook contain similar questions. The first reference, in brackets and italic, is to the old edition. The second reference is to the new edition
- **A summary of key points** so you can check that you have covered all the key concepts

Exam practice and using the answers

An exam style practice paper at the back of the book will help you make sure that you are totally exam-ready. This paper is exactly the same length and standard as your actual Stage 1 exam.

Answers to all the questions are provided at the back of the book. Once you have completed an exercise you can use the answers to check whether you have made any mistakes. You need to show full working in your exam – it isn't enough to write down the answer.

> **Which edition am I using?**
>
> The new editions of the *Edexcel GCSE Maths* core textbooks have yellow cover flashes saying "ideal for the 2001 specification". You can also use the old edition (no yellow cover flash) to help you prepare for your Stage 1 exam.

Contents

1 Integers   1
1.1   Face value and place value   NA2a   1
1.2   Reading, writing and ordering numbers   NA2a   1
1.3   Number lines   NA2a   3
1.4   Adding and subtracting   NA3a, NA3j   4
1.5   Multiplying and dividing   NA3a   5
1.6   Brackets and order of operations   NA3b   6
1.7   Rounding numbers   NA2a, NA3h   7
1.8   Factors, multiples and common factors   NA2a   8
1.9   Negative numbers   NA2a   9

2 Fractions and decimals   13
2.1   Improper fractions and mixed numbers   NA2c   13
2.2   Equivalent fractions   NA2c   14
2.3   Ordering fractions   NA2c   15
2.4   Multiplying fractions   NA3c, NA3d   16
2.5   Finding a fraction of a quantity   NA3c   17
2.6   Decimal place value   NA2d   17
2.7   Ordering decimals   NA2d   18
2.8   Adding and subtracting decimals   NA3a, NA3i, NA3j 19
2.9   Multiplying and dividing decimals by powers of 10 NA3a, NA3i   20
2.10 Fractions and decimals   NA3c, NA2d   21

3 Percentages and ratio   25
3.1   Understanding percentages   NA2e   25
3.2   Comparing different proportions using percentages NA2e   26
3.3   Working out a percentage of an amount   NA2e   27
3.4   Simplifying ratios   NA2f   28
3.5   Ratio, proportion and scale   NA2f   29

4 Algebra – structure and symbols   32
4.1   Writing expressions   NA5b   32
4.2   Collecting like terms   NA5b   33
4.3   Simplifying products   NA5b   34
4.4   Order of operations   NA5b   35
4.5   Expanding brackets   NA5b   35
4.6   Equations   NA5a   36

5 Algebra – coordinates   39
5.1   Inequalities   N/A   39
5.2   Read and plot coordinates in the first quadrant NA6b, S3e   40
5.3   Read and plot coordinates in all four quadrants NA6b, S3e   41
5.4   1-D, 2-D or 3-D?   S3e   42

6 Angles and construction   44
6.1   Right, acute and obtuse angles   S2b   44
6.2   Parallel and perpendicular   S2a, S2c   46

6.3	Measuring, drawing and estimating angles	S2b, S4d	47
6.4	Constructions	S4d	49
6.5	Bearings	S4b	50

7 Quadrilaterals and circles | | | 53 |
| 7.1 | Quadrilaterals | S2f | 53 |
| 7.2 | Circles | S2i | 55 |

8 Symmetry and transformations | | | 57 |
8.1	Reflective symmetry in 2-D shapes	S3a, S3b	57
8.2	Rotational symmetry	S3a, S3b	60
8.3	Rotation	S3a, S3b	62
8.4	Reflection	S3a, S3b	66

9 Scale and conversions | | | 69 |
9.1	Time		69
9.2	Reading scales	S4a	70
9.3	Choosing suitable units	S4a	71
9.4	Estimating	S4a	72
9.5	Converting between metric units	S4a	74

10 Handling data – collecting data | | | 76 |
| 10.1 | Designing questions and collecting data | H3a/H3b | 76 |

11 Handling data – representing and interpreting data | | | 81 |
11.1	Tally charts, bar charts, pictograms and pie charts	H4a, H5b	81
11.2	Measures of averages and spread	H4b	86
11.3	Interpretation and implications	H5b, H5j	88

12 Probability | | | 93 |
12.1	The probability scale	H4c	93
12.2	Mutually exclusive outcomes	H5g	96
12.3	Listing outcomes	H4e	98

Examination-style practice paper | | | 102 |
Answers | | | 105 |

Heinemann Educational Publishers,
Halley Court, Jordan Hill, Oxford, OX2 8EJ
a division of Reed Educational & Professional Publishing Ltd
Heinemann is a registered trademark of Reed Educational & Professional Publishing Ltd

OXFORD   MELBOURNE   AUCKLAND
JOHANNESBURG   BLANTYRE   GABORONE
IBADAN   PORTSMOUTH NH (USA)   CHICAGO

First published 2001

ISBN 0 435 53542 0

05   04   03   02
10   9   8   7   6   5   4   3

Designed and typeset by Tech-Set Ltd, Gateshead, Tyne and Wear
Cover photo: Stone Picture Library
Cover design by Miller, Craig and Cocking
Printed in the United Kingdom by Scotprint

Acknowledgements
The publishers and authors would like to thank Jean Linsky for her contribution and assistance with the manuscript.

The answers are not the responsibility of Edexcel.

Publishing team
Editorial
Sue Bennett
Lauren Bourque
Des Brady
Nicholas Georgiou
Carol Harris
Maggie Rumble
Nick Sample
Harry Smith

Design
Phil Richards
Colette Jacquelin

Production
David Lawrence
Jason Wyatt

Author team
Karen Hughes
Trevor Johnson
Peter Jolly
David Kent
Keith Pledger

Tel: 01865 888058 www.heinemann.co.uk

1 Integers – 4 rules, rounding, ordering

1.1 Face value and place value

Teaching reference:
(p 1, section 1.1)

■ Each digit in a number has a face value and a place value.

Example 1

Draw a place value diagram and write in
(a) a three digit number with a 2 in the Tens column
(b) a five digit number with a 6 in the Thousands column.

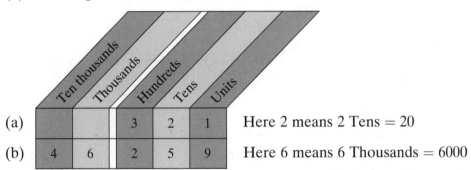

(a) Here 2 means 2 Tens = 20

(b) Here 6 means 6 Thousands = 6000

Exercise 1A   **Links (1A) 1A**

1   Draw a place value diagram and write in
     (a) a two digit number with a 3 in the Tens column
     (b) a four digit number with a 2 in the Hundreds column
     (c) a five digit number with a 1 in the Units column and a 3
          in the Hundreds column
     (d) a three digit number with a 4 in the Hundreds column
          and a 2 in the Tens column
     (e) a five digit number with a 3 in the Thousands column and
          a 2 in the Tens column.

2   Write down the value of the 5 in
     (a) 2502   **(b)** 351   **(c)** 54 321
     (d) 15   **(e)** 5489   **(f)** 10 050

1.2 Reading, writing and ordering numbers

Teaching reference:
pp 2–6, section 2.2

Example 2

(a) Write 37 802 in words.
(b) Write the number five thousand three hundred and five in
    figures.

(a)

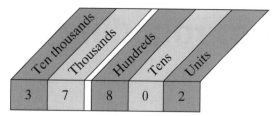

Thirty seven thousand eight hundred and two.

(b) Five thousand three hundred and five:

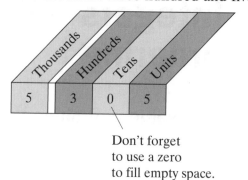

Don't forget
to use a zero
to fill empty space.

Exercise 1B   Links (*1B*) 1B

1 Write down the following numbers in words:
   (a) 237   **(b)** 6502   **(c)** 10302   **(d)** 321   **(e)** 15

2 Write down the following numbers in figures:
   (a) Three hundred and twenty three.
   (b) Six thousand two hundred and four.
   (c) Forty two.
   (d) Sixteen thousand seven hundred and thirty two.
   (e) Nine hundred and ninety nine.

3 The table below shows some prices of second-hand cars.
   Write down the price of each car in words.

Car	Price
Corsa	£7 995
Astra	£11 495
Clio	£4 835
Fiesta	£6 549
Puma	£13 205

Example 3

Put the following numbers in order of size, starting with the biggest:

   4532   4621   5831   425

In order of size starting with the biggest:

   5831   4621   4532   425

Exercise 1C   Links (*1B*) 1B

1 Put the following sets of numbers in order of size, starting with
   the biggest number:
   (a) 18, 324, 3450, 67.   **(b)** 234, 2681, 256, 963.
   (c) 10002, 6554, 9999, 9460.   **(d)** 56 762, 59 342, 56 745, 56 321.

2 The table below gives the prices of some second hand cars.
Rewrite the list in price order starting with the highest.

Car	Price
Corsa	£7 995
Astra	£11 495
Clio	£4 835
Fiesta	£6 549
Puma	£13 205

3 The attendances at the last five home matches for Liverpool
football club are written below:

> 37 992   43 845   43 621   39 042   39 681

Rewrite in order of size, starting with the largest attendance.

1.3 Number lines

- **Number lines can be used to show the position of a number.**

- **Number lines can be used to show the position of a number after it has been increased or decreased.**

Example 4

Use a number line to

(a) increase 6 by 4
(b) decrease 23 by 8.

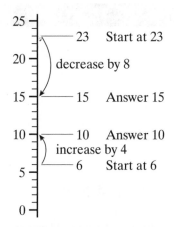

Exercise 1D   **Links 1C**

1 Draw a number line from 0 to 30.
Mark these numbers on the number line:
(a) 6   (b) 23   (c) 15   (d) 0   (e) 29

2 Use a number line from 0 to 25 to
(a) increase 6 by 3   (b) decrease 15 by 7   (c) increase 11 by 7
(d) increase 17 by 8   (e) decrease 19 by 13   (f) decrease 16 by 8.

3 For each of the following moves write down whether the move
is an increase or decrease, and by how much:
(a) 10 to 6   (b) 15 to 21   (c) 10 to 3   (d) 24 to 29   (e) 13 to 5   (f) 19 to 25.

1.4 Adding and subtracting

■ Some words that show you have to add numbers
  are *add*, *plus*, *total* and *sum*.

■ Some words that show you have to subtract numbers are
  subtract, *minus*, *take away* and *difference*.

■ If the numbers are too big to add or subtract in your head you
  can set the question out in columns.

Example 5

(a) Add 3, 6 and 9.
(b) Take 6 away from 15.
(c) Find the sum of 58 and 84.
(d) Find the difference between 382 and 157.

(a) $3 + 6 + 9 = 18$

(b) $15 - 6 = 9$

(c)
$$\begin{array}{r} 84 \\ 58\, + \\ \hline 142 \\ \hline \scriptstyle 1\ \ 1 \end{array}$$

(d)
$$\begin{array}{r} 3\overset{7}{\cancel{8}}\overset{1}{2} \\ 157 \\ \hline 225 \\ \hline \end{array}$$

Exercise 1E	Links (*1C, 1D, 1G*) 1D, 1E

1 Add 6, 4 and 2.

2 Subtract 7 from 18.

3 Find the total of 3, 4, 9 and 10.

4 16 minus 5.

5 54 plus 97.

6 134 take away 67.

7 Karen buys 3 different cakes. They cost 27p, 34p and 52p.
   Find the total cost of the cakes.

8 In four English tests Graham scores 89, 63, 42 and 24 marks.
   How many marks does Graham score altogether?

9 Julie has a collection of 325 badges. She gives 178 away to her
   friend. How many badges does she have left?

10 A school has 867 pupils. 498 pupils are girls. How many pupils
   in the school are boys?

11 Find the sum of 623, 125 and 689.

12 Find the difference between 823 and 697.

13 Eryl has 87 CDs and Luisa has 139 CDs. How many CDs do
   they have in total?

14 A book has 1142 pages. Veronica has read 738. How many
   pages does she have left to read?

1.5 Multiplying and dividing

Teaching reference: pp 10–11, section 1.3

■ Some words that show you have to multiply numbers are *times*, *product* and *multiply*.

■ Some words that show you have to divide numbers are *share* and *divide*.

Example 6
(a) Find the product of 3 and 6.
(c) Multiply 23 and 4.

(b) Share 36 by 4.
(d) Divide 84 by 3.

(a) $3 \times 6 = 18$
(c) $\begin{array}{r} 23 \\ 4 \times \\ \hline 92 \\ \hline {\scriptstyle 1} \end{array}$

(b) $36 \div 4 = 9$
(d) $\begin{array}{r} 2\,8 \\ 3\overline{)8^2 4} \end{array}$

Exercise 1F   Links (*1E*, *1F*, *1G*) 1F, 1G

1 Find the product of 8 and 6.

2 Multiply 19 and 5.   3 Divide 27 by 3.

4 $45 \div 9$ 5 82×6

6 15×10 7 234×100

8 Lesley buys 16 boxes of cakes. Each box contains 5 cakes. How many cakes does she buy?

9 Three friends share a packet of sweets. There are 81 sweets in the packet. How many sweets does each person receive?

10 A school hires 8 coaches for a trip to Alton Towers. Each coach holds 53 passengers. How many people can go to Alton Towers?

11 To complete a 200 m swimming race Jo has to swim 8 lengths of the swimming pool. How long is the swimming pool?

12 A soap opera is broadcast 4 times a week. How many programmes will be broadcast in a year? (A year has 52 weeks.)

13 A lottery syndicate of 4 people share a win of £7832. How much does each person receive?

14 Each volume of an encyclopaedia has 1524 pages. There are 8 volumes in the encyclopaedia.
    How many pages are there in the encyclopaedia altogether?

1.6 Brackets and order of operations

- Always work out brackets first. Then divide, multiply, add and subtract.
- When signs are the same do them in the order they appear.

Teaching reference:
pp 28–29, section 2.8

Example 7

Find the value of:

(a) $6 + 3 \times 2$
(b) $(6 + 8) \div 2$
(c) $(12 - 3) \times (4 + 3)$

(a) $6 + 3 \times 2$ (multiply first)

    $= 6 + 6$
    $= 12$

(b) $(6 + 8) \div 2$ (brackets first)

    $= 14 \div 2$
    $= 7$

(c) $(12 - 3) \times (4 + 3)$ (brackets first)

    $= \quad 9 \quad \times \quad 7$
    $= 63$

Exercise 1G   Links (*2H*) 2H

1   Find the value of
     (a) $6 + (3 \times 2)$
     (b) $7 - 3 - 2$
     (c) $18 \div (2 + 4)$
     (d) $(3 \times 2) \div (5 - 2)$
     (e) $36 \div 4 - 2$
     (f) $5 + 2 \times 4$
     (g) $3 + 2 \times 4 - 2$
     (h) $(2 \times 7) - (18 \div 3)$
     (i) $18 - 6 \times 2$
     (j) $9 \times 3 + (8 \div 2)$

2   Replace $*$ with $+$, $-$, $\times$ or $\div$ to make the following equations correct. Use brackets if you need to:
     (a) $7 * 3 = 21$
     (b) $2 * 3 * 4 = 14$
     (c) $3 * 5 * 2 = 21$
     (d) $10 * 4 * 2 = 3$

1.7 Rounding numbers

■ **To round to the nearest 10 look at the digit in the Units column:**
if it is less than 5 round down.
if it is 5 or more round up.

■ **To round to the nearest 100 look at the digit in the Tens column:**
if it is less than 5 round down.
if it is 5 or more round up.

■ **To round to the nearest 1000 look at the digit in the Hundreds column:**
if it is less than 5 round down.
if it is 5 or more round up.

Example 8

(a) Write 123 correct to the nearest 10.
(b) Write 374 correct to the nearest 100.
(c) Write 56 542 correct to the nearest 1000.

(a) 123 has a 3 in the Units column, which is less than 5, so round down.
123 correct to the nearest 10 is 120.
(b) 374 has a 7 in the Tens column, which is greater than 5, so round up.
374 correct to the nearest 100 is 400.
(c) 56 542 has a 5 in the Hundreds column, so round up.
56 542 correct to the nearest 1000 is 57 000.

Exercise 1H   **Links** (*1H*) **1I**

---

1 Write the following numbers correct to the nearest 10:
   (a) 12   (b) 18   (c) 6   (d) 67   (e) 75
   (f) 114   (g) 299   (h) 1055   (i) 2007   (j) 3145

2 Write the following numbers correct to the nearest 100:
   (a) 237   (b) 568   (c) 58   (d) 850   (e) 708
   (f) 3745   (g) 5955   (h) 9041   (i) 10 078   (j) 50 350

3 Write the following numbers correct to the nearest 1000:
   (a) 7892   (b) 6432   (c) 2500   (d) 4005   (e) 13 982
   (f) 16 432   (g) 156 540   (h) 784   (i) 500   (j) 372 450

4 Write each number correct to the nearest multiple of ten given in the brackets:
   (a) 13 (10)   (b) 25 (10)   (c) 76 (10)
   (d) 378 (100)   (e) 4759 (1000)   (f) 194 268 (10 000)
   (g) 364 582 (100)   (h) 2500 (1000)

5   Shefford High School has 1468 pupils. Write the number of pupils in the school correct to the nearest hundred.

6   47 891 people attended a rugby match. Write the attendance correct to the nearest 1000.

7   In 2001, 317 462 candidates took GCSE mathematics with Edexcel. Write the number of candidates correct to the nearest 10 000.

1.8 Factors, multiples and common factors

■   **A factor is a whole number that will divide into another number without a remainder.**

■   **Multiples of a number are made by multiplying that number by 1, 2, 3, 4 ... etc.**

■   **A common factor is a whole number which will divide into more than one other whole number without a remainder.**

Example 9

Write down all the factors of 12.

The numbers that will divide into 12 without a remainder are 1, 2, 3, 4, 6 and 12.

So the factors of 12 are 1, 2, 3, 4, 6 and 12.

Example 10

Write down the first 4 multiples of 4.

Multiplying 4 by 1, 2, 3 and 4 gives

    4   8   12   16

so the first 4 multiples of 4 are 4, 8, 12 and 16.

Example 11

Write down the common factors of 9 and 6.

    The factors of 9 are ①, ③, 9
    The factors of 6 are ①, 2, ③, 6

1 and 3 are factors of both 9 and 6. They are the common factors.

Exercise 1I	**Links (1K) 1L**

1   Write down all the factors of the following numbers:

(a)	6	**(b)**	10
(c)	15	**(d)**	17
(e)	27	**(f)**	36
(g)	90	**(h)**	120

2   Find the common factors of:
   (a) 4 and 6
   (b) 10 and 15
   (c) 24 and 36
   (d) 3 and 18
   (e) 10, 15 and 30.

3   List the first 5 multiples of:
   (a) 3
   (b) 7
   (c) 4
   (d) 10
   (e) 13

4

From the numbers in the cloud write down the numbers which are:
   (a) factors of 24
   (b) multiples of 5
   (c) factors of 16
   (d) multiples of 3
   (e) common factors of 16 and 24
   (f) common factors of 10 and 25.

1.9 Negative numbers

■   **We use negative numbers to represent quantities that are less than zero.**

Example 12
Write the largest and the smallest number in this list.

   3, −2, 0, −6, 8

−6 is the smallest number.
8 is the largest number.

Exercise 1J	**Links** (*10*) **1M**

1   Write the largest and the smallest number in each list.
   (a) −4, 0, 5, −8, 1   **(b)** −6, −3, 0, 10, 2
   (c) 8, −4, 1, 2, −9   **(d)** −3, −6, −18, −11, −1
   (e) −3, −11, 0, −2, −9

2 Use this number line to find the number that is:
(a) 3 more than −1   (b) 3 less than −1
(c) 6 less than 5   (d) 7 more than −2
(e) 8 more than −9   (f) 4 less than −4
(g) 4 more than 0   (h) 3 less than 0
(i) 7 less than −3   (j) 5 more than −8

3 What number is:
(a) 10 more than −20   (b) 30 less than −10
(c) 100 more than −300 (d) 200 less than 100
(e) 70 less than −150   (f) 300 less than 50
(g) 150 more than −500 (h) 80 more than −250
(i) 400 less than 70   (j) 180 more than −700

4 The table gives the highest and lowest temperatures for five days in one week.

	Mon	Tues	Weds	Thurs	Fri
Highest	11 °C	9 °C	3 °C	−2 °C	0 °C
Lowest	−1 °C	−4 °C	−6 °C	−8 °C	−7 °C

(a) On which day was the lowest temperature recorded?
(b) On which day was the highest temperature recorded?
(c) On which day was the difference between the highest temperature and lowest temperature the greatest?

5 A cable car runs from the bottom to the top of a mountain. The temperature at the bottom of the cable car is 3 °C. The temperature at the top of the cable car is 8 degrees less. What is the temperature at the top of the cable car?

Exercise 1K   Mixed questions

1 Write down the value of the underlined digit in each of these numbers:
(a) 2̲7   (b) 93̲   (c) 2̲74   (d) 67̲82   (e) 9̲536

2 The distances from Calais to some other European cities are given in the table below:

City	Distance
Brussels	204 km
Athens	3175 km
Bordeaux	845 km
Hanover	1096 km
Lisbon	2052 km

(a) Write the numbers in the list in words.
(b) Rewrite the list in order, starting with the city furthest away from Calais.

3 Draw a number line from 0 to 20. Show the following on your number line:
  (a) 6 increased by 3   (b) 12 decreased by 5
  (c) 8 increased by 6   (d) 20 decreased by 12
  (e) 13 decreased by 4   (f) 2 increased by 13.

4 (a) 7 plus 3.
  (b) 20 minus 6.
  (c) 13 times by 4.
  (d) 27 shared by 3.
  (e) Find the total of 6, 10, 23.
  (f) Sum 28, 57 and 39.
  (g) Find the difference between 237 and 93.
  (h) Multiply 132 by 8.
  (i) Divide 480 by 3.

> Do not use a calculator for this exercise.

5 A snooker player plays 3 games. He scores 97, 104 and 86. Find his total score.

> Do not use a calculator for this exercise.

6 226 g of flour is taken from a 1 kg bag of flour. How much flour is left in the bag? (1 kg = 1000 g.)

> Do not use a calculator for this exercise.

7 1862 people pay £8 each to see a film. How much money is collected altogether?

> Do not use a calculator for this exercise.

8 A builder can carry 8 bricks. How many trips will the builder need to make to move a pile of 952 bricks?

> Do not use a calculator for this exercise.

9 Find the value of:
  (a) $3 + 2 \times 5$ (b) $6 + (3 + 8)$ (c) $(6 \times 7) \div 3$
  (d) $8 - 18 \div 3$ (e) $(5 + 3) \times (8 - 4)$

10 Write down each number correct to the nearest multiple of ten given in the brackets:
  (a) 236 (10)   (b) 6892 (100)   (c) 9823 (100)
  (d) 5545 (1000)   (e) 2378 (1000)   (f) 6351 (100)

11 Here is a list of numbers:
        6, 7, 8, 9, 10, 11, 12, 13, 14, 15
  From the list of numbers write down all the numbers that are:
  (a) factors of 18
  (b) factors of 14
  (c) multiples of 3
  (d) multiples of 6
  (e) common factors of 24 and 36
  (f) common factors of 14 and 21.

12 What number is:
  (a) 4 more than -2 (b) 6 less than 1
  (c) 11 more than 0   (d) 14 more than -7
  (e) 6 less than 0   (f) 30 more than -70
  (g) 25 less than -100 (h) 140 less than -50

Summary of key points

- Each digit in a number has a face value and a place value.

- Number lines can be used to show the position of a number.

- Number lines can be used to show the position of a number after it has been increased or decreased.

- Some words that show you have to add numbers are *add*, *plus*, *total* and *sum*.

- Some words that show you have to subtract numbers are *subtract*, *minus*, *take away* and *difference*.

- If the numbers are too big to add or subtract in your head you can set the question out in columns.

- Some words that show you have to multiply numbers are *times*, *product* and *multiply*.

- Some words that show you have to divide numbers are *share* and *divide*.

- Always work out brackets first. Then divide, multiply, add and subtract.

- When signs are the same do them in the order they appear.

- To round to the nearest power of ten look at the digit in the place value column to the right of that power of ten:
  if it is less than 5 round down.
  if it is 5 or more round up.

- A factor is a whole number that will divide into another number without a remainder.

- Multiples of a number are made by multiplying that number by 1, 2, 3, 4 ... etc.

- A common factor is a whole number which will divide into more than one other whole number without a remainder.

- Negative numbers represent quantities that are less than zero.

2 Fractions and decimals

2.1 Improper fractions and mixed numbers

Teaching reference: pp 65–68, sections 4.1, 4.2, 4.3

■ In a fraction:

The top number shows how many parts we want.

The top number is called the *numerator*.

$$\frac{3}{4}$$

The bottom number shows how many parts there are.

The bottom number is called the *denominator*.

■ Fractions with a larger numerator than denominator are called *improper* fractions.

■ An improper fraction can be written as a mixed number – a mixture of a fraction and a whole number.

Example 1
Change these improper fractions to mixed numbers:

(a) $\frac{17}{12}$ (b) $\frac{23}{8}$ (c) $\frac{7}{2}$

(a) $\frac{17}{12} = \frac{12}{12} + \frac{5}{12} = 1\frac{5}{12}$ (b) $\frac{23}{8} = \frac{8}{8} + \frac{8}{8} + \frac{7}{8} = 2\frac{7}{8}$ (c) $\frac{7}{2} = \frac{2}{2} + \frac{2}{2} + \frac{2}{2} + \frac{1}{2} = 3\frac{1}{2}$

Example 2
Change these mixed numbers into improper fractions:

(a) $1\frac{3}{4}$ (b) $2\frac{1}{5}$

(a) $1\frac{3}{4} = \frac{4}{4} + \frac{3}{4} = \frac{7}{4}$

(b) $2\frac{1}{5} = \frac{5}{5} + \frac{5}{5} + \frac{1}{5} = \frac{11}{5}$

Exercise 2A   Links (*4C*) 4C

1 Change these improper fractions into mixed numbers:

(a) $\frac{5}{4}$ (b) $\frac{3}{2}$ (c) $\frac{7}{5}$ (d) $\frac{9}{7}$ (e) $\frac{13}{11}$

(f) $\frac{5}{2}$ (g) $\frac{11}{5}$ (h) $\frac{13}{5}$ (i) $\frac{17}{7}$ (j) $\frac{20}{8}$

(k) $\frac{9}{2}$ (l) $\frac{13}{4}$ (m) $\frac{17}{6}$ (n) $\frac{19}{4}$ (o) $\frac{23}{3}$

2 Change these mixed numbers to improper fractions:

(a) $1\frac{1}{5}$ (b) $1\frac{3}{7}$ (c) $1\frac{3}{4}$ (d) $1\frac{1}{2}$ (e) $1\frac{3}{10}$

(f) $2\frac{4}{5}$ (g) $2\frac{2}{3}$ (h) $2\frac{1}{4}$ (i) $2\frac{5}{9}$ (j) $2\frac{6}{7}$

(k) $3\frac{1}{3}$ (l) $3\frac{3}{4}$ (m) $4\frac{2}{10}$ (n) $5\frac{1}{3}$ (o) $5\frac{7}{10}$

2.2 Equivalent fractions

Teaching reference:
pp 68–70, section 4.4
pp 71–73, section 4.6

■ **Fractions can be simplified if the numerator and denominator have a common factor. When all common factors are cancelled the fraction is in its simplest form.**

$$\frac{24}{36} = \frac{6}{9} = \frac{2}{3}$$

(÷4) (÷3) across the top, (÷4) (÷3) across the bottom

■ **Equivalent fractions are fractions that have the same value.**

$\frac{3}{4} = \frac{6}{8} = \frac{12}{16}$

Example 3

Write the fraction $\frac{18}{24}$ in its simplest form.

$$\frac{18}{24} = \frac{3}{4}$$

÷6 (top and bottom)

Example 4

Change $\frac{3}{7}$ to an equivalent fraction with a denominator of 21.

$$\frac{3}{7} \quad \boxed{\text{3 multiplied by 3 is 9}} \quad \boxed{\text{7 multiplied by 3 is 21}} = \frac{9}{21}$$

| **Exercise 2B** | **Links (4D, 4F) 4D, 4F** |

1 Write the following fractions in their simplest form by finding common factors:

 (a) $\frac{6}{8}$ **(b)** $\frac{12}{15}$ **(c)** $\frac{16}{24}$ **(d)** $\frac{25}{35}$ **(e)** $\frac{18}{27}$

2 Copy the table below.
 Draw lines to join the equivalent fractions.

$\frac{1}{5}$	$\frac{5}{8}$
$\frac{3}{4}$	$\frac{12}{16}$
$\frac{15}{24}$	$\frac{3}{7}$
$\frac{5}{10}$	$\frac{3}{15}$
$\frac{6}{14}$	$\frac{1}{2}$
$\frac{2}{5}$	$\frac{8}{20}$

3 Copy these sets of fractions. Fill in the missing numbers to make the fractions equivalent.

(a) $\frac{2}{5} = \frac{}{10} = \frac{}{20} = \frac{}{30} = \frac{}{100}$ (b) $\frac{1}{6} = \frac{}{12} = \frac{4}{} = \frac{}{30} = \frac{8}{}$ (c) $\frac{3}{8} = \frac{}{48} = \frac{12}{} = \frac{}{24}$

4 Write down two fractions equivalent to

(a) $\frac{4}{5}$ (b) $\frac{27}{36}$ (c) $\frac{8}{12}$ (d) $\frac{1}{9}$

2.3 Ordering fractions

Teaching reference:
(pp 60–61, section 4.7)
pp 73–74, section 4.7

■ **To put a list of fractions in order of size rewrite them as equivalent fractions with the same denominator, then use the numerator to put them in order.**

Example 5

List the following fractions in order, starting with the largest:

$$\frac{1}{3}, \frac{2}{5}, \frac{3}{10}, \frac{1}{6}$$

Rewrite the fractions with a common denominator of 30:

$$\frac{1}{3} = \frac{10}{30} \qquad \frac{2}{5} = \frac{12}{30} \qquad \frac{3}{10} = \frac{9}{30} \qquad \frac{1}{6} = \frac{5}{30}$$

In order:

$$\frac{12}{30}, \frac{10}{30}, \frac{9}{30}, \frac{5}{30} \qquad \text{or} \qquad \frac{2}{5}, \frac{1}{3}, \frac{3}{10}, \frac{1}{6}$$

Exercise 2C   Links *(4G)* 4G

1 Which is larger:

(a) $\frac{1}{4}$ or $\frac{1}{5}$ (b) $\frac{2}{3}$ or $\frac{3}{5}$ (c) $\frac{7}{10}$ or $\frac{11}{15}$ (d) $\frac{6}{7}$ or $\frac{2}{3}$?

2 Write these fractions in ascending order.
(Hint: use a common denominator of 20.)

$$\frac{1}{2}, \frac{2}{5}, \frac{3}{10}, \frac{1}{4}$$

3 Keith eats $\frac{1}{3}$ of a cake, Mary eats $\frac{1}{4}$ of the same cake. Who eats the largest piece?

4 A book is divided into 4 sections. The table below shows what fraction of the book each section is:

Section 1	$\frac{1}{8}$
Section 2	$\frac{2}{3}$
Section 3	$\frac{1}{6}$
Section 4	$\frac{1}{24}$

(a) Which section is the largest?   (b) Which section is the smallest?

5 Write the fractions $\frac{7}{8}, \frac{13}{16}, \frac{1}{4}, \frac{2}{3}$ in descending order.

2.4 Multiplying fractions

■ **To multiply two fractions:**

Multiply numerators.

$$\frac{3}{4} \times \frac{4}{7} = \frac{12}{28}$$

Multiply denominators.

■ **To multiply a fraction by a whole number:**

Multiply the numerator by the whole number.

$$\frac{5}{6} \times 3 = \frac{15}{6}$$

The denominator stays the same.

■ **After multiplying fractions you should simplify the answer if you can.**

Teaching reference:
(*pp 66–67, section 4.10*)
pp 79–81, section 4.10

Example 6

Work out

(a) $\frac{2}{3} \times \frac{3}{5}$ (b) $\frac{1}{2} \times \frac{3}{7}$ (c) $\frac{2}{3} \times 4$ (d) $\frac{1}{6} \times 3$

(a) $\frac{2}{3} \times \frac{3}{5} = \frac{2 \times 3}{3 \times 5} = \frac{6}{15} = \frac{2}{5}$ (b) $\frac{1}{2} \times \frac{3}{7} = \frac{1 \times 3}{2 \times 7} = \frac{3}{14}$

(c) $\frac{2}{3} \times 4 = \frac{2 \times 4}{3} = \frac{8}{3} = 2\frac{2}{3}$ (d) $\frac{1}{6} \times 3 = \frac{1 \times 3}{6} = \frac{3}{6} = \frac{1}{2}$

Exercise 2D   Links (*4J*) 4J

1 Work out

   (a) $\frac{2}{5} \times \frac{3}{4}$ (b) $\frac{1}{2} \times \frac{2}{7}$ (c) $\frac{1}{3} \times \frac{3}{7}$ (d) $\frac{3}{7} \times \frac{1}{5}$

   (e) $\frac{2}{3} \times \frac{2}{5}$ (f) $\frac{3}{8} \times \frac{1}{4}$ (g) $\frac{5}{9} \times \frac{1}{4}$ (h) $\frac{2}{11} \times \frac{1}{2}$

   (i) $\frac{5}{8} \times \frac{2}{3}$ (j) $\frac{4}{5} \times \frac{1}{6}$

2 Work out

   (a) $\frac{2}{3} \times 4$ (b) $\frac{3}{5} \times 2$ (c) $\frac{5}{8} \times 6$ (d) $\frac{1}{2} \times 7$

   (e) $4 \times \frac{2}{7}$ (f) $5 \times \frac{3}{10}$ (g) $3 \times \frac{2}{5}$ (h) $4 \times \frac{4}{7}$

3 One centimetre is about $\frac{1}{2}$ inch. How many inches are there in 7 cm?

4 A bottle of lemonade contains $\frac{7}{10}$ of a litre of lemonade. How many litres of lemonade are there in 6 bottles?

5 A can holds $\frac{1}{3}$ of a litre of coke. How much coke is there in 10 cans?

6 Samina's Maths lesson is $\frac{3}{4}$ hour long. She has 3 lessons a week. How long does Samina spend in Maths lessons during 1 week?

2.5 Finding a fraction of a quantity

■ **To find a fraction of a quantity multiply the quantity by the fraction.**

Example 7

(a) Find $\frac{2}{3}$ of 9.

(b) A cake weighs 300 g. How much does $\frac{1}{6}$ of the cake weigh?

(a) $\frac{2}{3}$ of $9 = \frac{2}{3} \times 9 = \frac{18}{3} = 6$ (b) $\frac{1}{6}$ of $300\,g = \frac{1}{6} \times 300 = \frac{300}{6} = 50\,g$

Exercise 2E	Links (*4E*) 4E

1 Work out:

    (a) $\frac{3}{4}$ of 12   **(b)** $\frac{2}{5}$ of 10   **(c)** $\frac{2}{3}$ of 15   **(d)** $\frac{5}{7}$ of 28

    (e) $\frac{3}{8}$ of 32   **(f)** $\frac{4}{11}$ of 22   **(g)** $\frac{5}{9}$ of 36   **(h)** $\frac{2}{3}$ of 60

2 A pizza weighs 400 g. How much does $\frac{1}{8}$ of a pizza weigh?

3 There are 24 houses in Lancaster Place. $\frac{3}{4}$ of the houses have garages. How many houses have garages?

4 Liverpool played 48 matches last season. They won $\frac{5}{6}$ of these matches. How many matches did they win?

5 The normal price of a dress is £36. In a sale the dress is sold for $\frac{2}{3}$ of its normal price. How much does the dress cost in the sale?

6 A class of 28 pupils took a Maths test. $\frac{3}{4}$ of the pupils passed the test. How many pupils passed the test?

2.6 Decimal place value

Teaching reference: pp 99–100, section 6.1

■ **In a decimal number the decimal point separates the whole number from the part that is smaller than 1.**

Example 8

Write down the value of the underlined digit in each number:

(a) 4$\underline{1}$.3   (b) 0.28$\underline{5}$ (c) 16.8$\underline{9}$

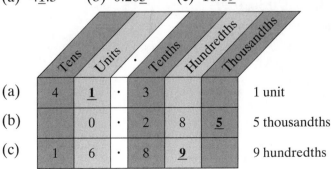

(a) 4 $\underline{1}$ · 3   1 unit

(b)   0 · 2 8 $\underline{5}$ 5 thousandths

(c) 1 6 · 8 $\underline{9}$ 9 hundredths

Exercise 2F   **Links (6A) 6A**

1 Draw a place value diagram like the one in Example **8** and write in these numbers:
   (**a**) 5.82   (**b**) 7.801   (**c**) 19.1   (**d**) 20.02
   (**e**) 13.381   (**f**) 0.76   (**g**) 0.5   (**h**) 0.001

2 Write down the value of the underlined digit in each number:
   (**a**) 10.3$\underline{2}$ (**b**) 11.19$\underline{2}$ (**c**) 0.$\underline{7}$6   (**d**) 0.80$\underline{1}$
   (**e**) $\underline{1}$.308   (**f**) 7.$\underline{9}$2   (**g**) 0.00$\underline{1}$ (**h**) 1.00$\underline{2}$
   (**i**) $\underline{1}$2.3   (**j**) 15.$\underline{8}$9

3 Write down the value of the 6 in each of these numbers:
   (**a**) 0.062   (**b**) 2.631   (**c**) 6.21   (**d**) 60.82   (**e**) 0.006

2.7 Ordering decimals

Teaching reference:
pp 100–102, section 6.2

■ **You can sort decimals in order of size by first comparing the whole numbers, then the digits in the tenths place, then the digits in the hundredths place, and so on.**

Example 9
Write these decimal numbers in order of size, starting with the largest:

   0.36   2.5   0.58   0.621   0.003

		largest value digit
In order:	2.5	(2 units)
	0.621	(6 tenths)
	0.58	(5 tenths)
	0.36	(3 tenths)
	0.003	(3 thousandths)

Exercise 2G   **Links (*some of 6A*) 6B**

1 Rearrange these decimal numbers in order of size, starting with the largest:
   (**a**) 2.1, 3.68, 0.20, 0.03   (**b**) 0.76, 0.75, 0.07, 0.001
   (**c**) 9.08, 0.98, 0.09, 9.009   (**d**) 6.01, 1.06, 0.016, 0.61
   (**e**) 0.9, 0.09, 0.009, 9.0   (**f**) 0.03, 30.0, 0.30, 0.303

2 The times of five runners in a 100 m race are given below:

John	10.96 s
Douglas	11.02 s
Matt	10.93 s
Colin	11.13 s
Graham	10.87 s

Rewrite the list in order, starting with the fastest time.

3 A sports drink can lists the following amounts of vitamins per 100 ml of the drink:

B2	0.08 mg
Niacin	0.89 mg
B6	0.10 mg
Pantothenic acid	0.30 mg

Rewrite the list of vitamins in order, starting with the largest amount.

4 The table gives the heights in metres of five basketball players:

Karim	Peter	Leroy	Curtis	Greg
2.10	1.92	2.15	1.96	2.06

Write the list of names in descending order of height (starting with the tallest).

2.8 Adding and subtracting decimals

Teaching reference: pp 104–106, section 6.4

■ **When adding and subtracting decimals make sure that you keep the numbers in their correct place value column.**

Example 10

(a) $15.6 + 5.24$
(b) $1.3 - 0.24$

(a)
$$\begin{array}{r} 15.6 \\ + \ 5.24 \\ \hline 20.84 \\ \hline \end{array}$$
1 |

Keep the decimal points in line.

(b)
$$\begin{array}{r} \overset{2\ 1}{1.\cancel{3}0} \\ - \ 0.24 \\ \hline 1.06 \\ \hline \end{array}$$
— Fill any gaps with zero.

Exercise 2H   **Links (6C, 6D, 6E) 6D, 6E, 6F**

Do not use a calculator for these exercises.

1 Work out:
(a) $5.3 + 2.6$ (b) $4.5 + 0.7$ (c) $2.13 + 3.14$ (d) $0.32 + 0.49$
(e) $1.2 + 1.58$ (f) $6.94 + 0.7$ (g) $30.8 + 2.79$ (h) $23.1 + 0.23$
(i) $5.78 + 0.031$ (j) $21.3 + 0.02$

2 Work out:
(a) $7.8 - 3.6$ (b) $6.1 - 2.9$ (c) $18.2 - 0.7$ (d) $9.23 - 1.8$
(e) $6.2 - 2.34$ (f) $2.9 - 0.36$ (g) $15.1 - 1.51$ (h) $20.01 - 6.2$
(i) $9 - 3.62$ (j) $0.36 - 0.036$

3 Karen is making some cakes for a party. She uses 1.5 kg of flour, 0.75 kg of margarine and 0.325 kg of sugar. What is the total weight of these ingredients?

4 A set of triplets weigh 2.3 kg, 2 kg and 2.05 kg at birth. What is their total birth weight?

5 A relay team runs a race. The times for the four runners are 10.02 seconds, 10.3 seconds, 9.98 seconds and 10 seconds. How long does the whole team take to run the race?

6 Mary takes 0.375 kg of flour from a packet of flour. The packet weighs 1.5 kg when full. How much flour is left?

7 A 400 m runner completes a race in 44.2 seconds. His time at 200 metres was 23.04 seconds. How long did the runner take to run the second 200 metres?

2.9 Multiplying and dividing decimals by powers of 10 and less than 10

Teaching reference: pp 106–108, sections 6.5, 6.6

■ **To multiply decimal numbers by 10 move the digits 1 place to the left.**

■ **To multiply decimal numbers by 100 move the digits 2 places to the left.**

■ **To multiply decimal numbers by 1000 move the digits 3 places to the left.**

■ **To divide decimal numbers by 10 move the digits 1 place to the right.**

■ **To divide decimal numbers by 100 move the digits 2 places to the right.**

■ **To divide decimal numbers by 1000 move the digits 3 places to the right.**

Example 11
Work out:

(a) 3.14×10
(b) $6.89 \div 10$
(c) 0.361×100
(d) $2.36 \div 100$
(e) $78.19 \div 1000$
(f) 2.3×1000

(a) $3.14 \times 10 = 31.4$
(b) $6.89 \div 10 = 0.689$
(c) $0.361 \times 100 = 36.1$
(d) $2.36 \div 100 = 0.0236$
(e) $78.19 \div 1000 = 0.07819$
(f) $2.3 \times 1000 = 2300$

Use zero to fill any columns that are empty.

Example 12

Work out:

(a) 13.4×3

(b) $8.19 \div 9$

(a) $134 \times 3 = 402$
$402 \div 10 = 40.2$
so $13.4 \times 3 = 40.2$

$(134 = 13.4 \times 10$, so 402
is ten times too big).

(b) $8.19 \div 9$
$819 \div 9 = 91$
$91 \div 100 = 0.91$
so $8.19 \div 9 = 0.91$

$(819 = 8.19 \times 100$, so 91 is a
hundred times too big).

Exercise 2I Links (*6F*) 6G, 6H, 6I

Do not use a calculator in these exercises.

1 Work out:
 (**a**) 2.1×10
 (**b**) 0.1×100
 (**c**) 2.3×10
 (**d**) 0.017×100
 (**e**) 0.28×1000
 (**f**) 3.1×10
 (**g**) 4.6×100
 (**h**) 0.36×1000
 (**i**) 3.14×100
 (**j**) 3.14×1000

2 Work out:
 (**a**) $28.1 \div 10$
 (**b**) $36.9 \div 100$
 (**c**) $6.89 \div 10$
 (**d**) $123.1 \div 1000$
 (**e**) $23.1 \div 100$
 (**f**) $0.23 \div 10$
 (**g**) $1.3 \div 100$
 (**h**) $3.14 \div 10$
 (**i**) $3.14 \div 100$
 (**j**) $0.02 \div 1000$

3 Work out:
 (**a**) 2.1×10
 (**b**) $6.2 \div 10$
 (**c**) 0.162×1000
 (**d**) $3.89 \div 100$
 (**e**) 0.3×100
 (**f**) $2.38 \div 1000$
 (**g**) 0.35×100
 (**h**) $0.2 \div 1000$

4 Work out:
 (**a**) 8.3×4
 (**b**) 2.5×6
 (**c**) 11.1×5
 (**d**) 3.11×4
 (**e**) 2.31×8
 (**f**) $18.2 \div 2$
 (**g**) $28.4 \div 4$
 (**h**) $65.5 \div 5$
 (**i**) $6.48 \div 8$
 (**j**) $7.07 \div 7$

2.10 Fractions and decimals

Teaching reference:
(*pp 91–92, section 6.6*)
pp 109–110, section 6.7

■ **Fractions can be changed into decimals by dividing the
numerator by the denominator. Decimals can be changed into
fractions by using a place value table.**

Example 13

Write as a decimal:

(a) $\frac{2}{5}$

(b) $\frac{3}{8}$

(a) $2 \div 5 = 0.4$ $\frac{2}{5} = 0.4$

(b) $3 \div 8 = 0.375$ $\frac{3}{8} = 0.375$

Example 14

Write as a fraction:

(a) 0.3   (b) 0.281

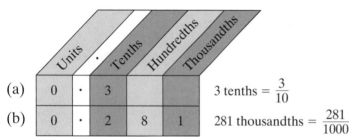

(a) 0 · 3   3 tenths $= \dfrac{3}{10}$

(b) 0 · 2 8 1   281 thousandths $= \dfrac{281}{1000}$

Exercise 2J   Links (*6I*) 6J

1   Change these fractions into decimals:

    (a) $\frac{1}{2}$ **(b)** $\frac{1}{4}$ **(c)** $\frac{3}{4}$ **(d)** $\frac{3}{5}$ **(e)** $\frac{7}{10}$

    (f) $\frac{11}{20}$ **(g)** $\frac{5}{8}$ **(h)** $\frac{17}{100}$ **(i)** $\frac{7}{8}$ **(j)** $\frac{4}{5}$

2   Change these decimals into fractions:

    (a) 0.3   **(b)** 0.6   **(c)** 0.21   **(d)** 0.36

    (e) 0.789   **(f)** 0.623   **(g)** 0.02   **(h)** 0.031

    (i) 0.007   **(j)** 0.203

Exercise 2K   Mixed questions

1   Change these improper fractions to mixed numbers:

    (a) $\frac{9}{8}$ **(b)** $\frac{15}{9}$ **(c)** $\frac{20}{6}$ **(d)** $\frac{25}{8}$

2   Change these mixed numbers to improper fractions:

    (a) $1\frac{1}{4}$ **(b)** $1\frac{2}{3}$ **(c)** $2\frac{2}{5}$ **(d)** $3\frac{5}{7}$

3   Write the following fractions in their simplest form:

    (a) $\frac{6}{8}$ **(b)** $\frac{9}{15}$ **(c)** $\frac{16}{18}$ **(d)** $\frac{24}{30}$

4   Fill in the missing numbers to make these fractions equivalent:

    (a) $\frac{3}{4} = \frac{}{12}$ **(b)** $\frac{5}{8} = \frac{}{16}$ **(c)** $\frac{}{4} = \frac{24}{32}$

    (d) $\frac{}{7} = \frac{6}{21}$ **(e)** $\frac{3}{} = \frac{12}{20}$ **(f)** $\frac{3}{8} = \frac{}{40}$

5   In a class of Year 11 students, $\frac{1}{5}$ of the students go home for lunch, $\frac{3}{4}$ eat sandwiches and $\frac{1}{20}$ eat school lunch.

    (a) What do the largest number of students do at lunchtime?

    (b) What do the smallest number of students do at lunchtime?

6   Write the fractions $\frac{1}{3}, \frac{3}{5}, \frac{3}{10}$ and $\frac{5}{6}$ in ascending order.

7 Work out (simplify where possible):

(a) $\frac{3}{7} \times \frac{2}{10}$ (b) $\frac{4}{5} \times \frac{3}{8}$ (c) $\frac{6}{7} \times \frac{5}{12}$

8 Work out:

(a) $\frac{3}{11} \times 5$ (b) $\frac{4}{7} \times 3$ (c) $6 \times \frac{2}{3}$

9 John has 4 pieces of homework. Each piece of homework should take $\frac{3}{4}$ hour. How long should John spend?

10 Work out:

(a) $\frac{3}{4}$ of 32   (b) $\frac{3}{5}$ of 15   (c) $\frac{2}{3}$ of 27

11 A coach holds 54 passengers. $\frac{2}{3}$ of the passengers are adults. How many passengers are adults?

12 Write down the value of the underlined digit:

(a) 11.3<u>8</u>   (b) 0.02<u>1</u>   (c) 1.0<u>3</u>2   (d) 0.6<u>8</u>

13 Write these numbers in ascending order:

8.078, 0.878, 0.087, 0.87, 0.8.

14 Without using a calculator, work out:

(a) $8.9 + 0.36$ (b) $6.89 - 1.36$ (c) $5 + 2.13$ (d) $1.3 - 0.24$
(e) $31.3 + 2.95$ (f) $7.8 - 0.78$ (g) $16.1 + 0.38$ (h) $10 - 2.93$

15 Without using a calculator, work out:

(a) 6.3×10 (b) $0.9 \div 10$ (c) 3.2×1000
(d) 17.91×100 (e) $11 \div 100$ (f) $2.36 \div 1000$

16 Without using a calculator, work out:

(a) 2.4×6 (b) 13.1×3 (c) 2.42×5
(d) $10.6 \div 2$ (e) $33.6 \div 3$ (f) $4.88 \div 8$

17 Write as decimals:

(a) $\frac{3}{4}$ (b) $\frac{1}{8}$ (c) $\frac{3}{10}$ (d) $\frac{13}{20}$ (e) $\frac{4}{5}$ (f) $\frac{27}{100}$

18 Write these decimal numbers as fractions:

(a) 0.7   (b) 0.381   (c) 0.27   (d) 0.03   (e) 0.021   (f) 0.002

Summary of key points

- **In a fraction:**

  The top number shows how many parts we want.   The top number is called the *numerator*.

  $$\frac{3}{4}$$

  The bottom number shows how many parts there are.   The bottom number is called the *denominator*.

- **Fractions with a larger numerator than denominator are called *improper* fractions.**

- **An improper fraction can be written as a mixed number – a mixture of a fraction and a whole number.**

- Fractions can be simplified if the numerator and denominator have a common factor. When all common factors are cancelled the fraction is in its simplest form.

- Equivalent fractions are fractions that have the same value.

- To put a list of fractions in order of size rewrite them as equivalent fractions with the same denominator, then use the numerators to put them in order.

- To multiply two fractions:

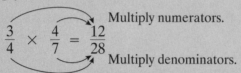

$$\frac{3}{4} \times \frac{4}{7} = \frac{12}{28}$$

Multiply numerators.

Multiply denominators.

- To multiply a fraction by a whole number:

Multiply the numerator by the whole number.

$$\frac{5}{6} \times 3 = \frac{15}{6}$$

The denominator stays the same.

- After multiplying fractions you should simplify the answer if you can.

- To find a fraction of a quantity multiply the quantity by the fraction.

- In a decimal the decimal point separates the whole number from the part that is less than 1.

- You can sort decimals into order of size by first comparing the whole numbers, then the digits in the tenths place, then the digits in the hundredths place, and so on.

- When adding and subtracting decimals make sure that you keep the numbers in their correct place value column.

- To multiply decimal numbers by 10 move the digits 1 place to the left.

- To multiply decimal numbers by 100 move the digits 2 places to the left.

- To multiply decimal numbers by 1000 move the digits 3 places to the left.

- To divide decimal numbers by 10 move the digits 1 place to the right.

- To divide decimal numbers by 100 move the digits 2 places to the right.

- To divide decimal numbers by 1000 move the digits 3 places to the right.

- Fractions can be changed into decimals by dividing the numerator by the denominator. Decimals can be changed into fractions by using a place value table.

3 Percentages and ratio

3.1 Understanding percentages

Teaching reference: pp 228–234, sections 14.1, 14.2

- Percentage
  %
  pc
  } means 'number of parts per hundred'.

- To write a percentage as a fraction, always use the denominator 100.

Example 1

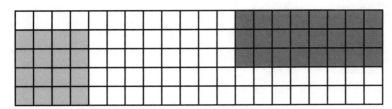

(a) What percentage of the rectangle is shaded light grey?
(b) What percentage of the rectangle is shaded dark grey?
(c) What percentage of the rectangle is not shaded?
(d) Write your answers to parts (a), (b) and (c) as fractions.

The rectangle is divided into 100 equal parts.
(a) 16 parts out of one hundred are shaded light grey.
16% of the rectangle is light grey.
(b) 24 parts are shaded dark grey. 24% of the rectangle is dark grey.
(c) 60 parts are unshaded. 60% of the rectangle is unshaded.
(d) $16\% = \frac{16}{100}$ $24\% = \frac{24}{100}$ $60\% = \frac{60}{100}$

Exercise 3A Links (*14A*) 14A, 14B, 14C

1

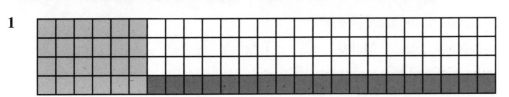

(a) What percentage of the rectangle is shaded light grey?
(b) What percentage of the rectangle is shaded dark grey?
(c) What percentage of the rectangle is not shaded?
(d) Write your answers to parts (a), (b) and (c) as fractions.

2   100 Year 11 students were asked to name their favourite sport.
The table below shows their replies:

Sport	No. of students
Football	63
Rugby	16
Basketball	18
Tennis	3

   (a) What percentage of the students chose football?
   (b) What percentage preferred tennis?
   (c) Write down the percentage and fraction who preferred rugby.

3   A cereal manufacturer lists the following nutritional
information on a packet of cornflakes.

	Typical value per 100 g
Carbohydrates	82 g
Fat	1 g
Protein	8 g

   (a) What percentage of a serving of cornflakes is carbohydrates?
   (b) What percentage of a serving of cornflakes is protein?
   (c) What percentage of a serving is something other than
carbohydrates, fat or protein?
   (d) Write your answers to parts **(a)**, **(b)** and **(c)** as fractions.

4   Draw a rectangle 20 cm long and 5 cm wide.
   (a) Shade 25% of the rectangle blue.
   (b) Shade 13% of the rectangle red.
   (c) What percentage of your rectangle is left unshaded?

3.2 Comparing different proportions using percentages

Example 2

In four class tests Karen scored 9 out of 10 in History, 13 out of 20
in French, 68 out of 100 in Mathematics and 35 out of 50 in English.
Which test did she do best in?

Karen's scores as fractions of the total marks are:

   History $\frac{9}{10}$ French $\frac{13}{20}$ Maths $\frac{68}{100}$ English $\frac{35}{50}$

These fractions can be changed to percentages by finding
equivalent fractions with a denominator of 100.

   History $\frac{9}{10} = \frac{90}{100} = 90\%$ French $\frac{13}{20} = \frac{65}{100} = 65\%$

   Maths $\frac{68}{100} = 68\%$ English $\frac{35}{50} = \frac{70}{100} = 70\%$

Karen did best in History with 90% and worst in French with 65%.

Exercise 3B   Links 14D

1   The number of games won by three football teams is shown
    below together with the total number of matches played:

Team	Played	Won
Greenfield FC	10	4
Millbrook Utd	5	3
Carrbrook Town	20	9

   (a) Write down the number of matches won by each team as
       a percentage of the games they played.
   (b) Which team is the most successful?

2   Jessica bought 3 packets of sweets. The packets were different
    sizes. She counted the numbers of the different flavoured
    sweets in each packet. The results are shown below:

	Packet 1 (20 sweets)	Packet 2 (50 sweets)	Packet 3 (100 sweets)
Strawberry	6	13	29
Blackcurrant	3	6	6
Lime	7	24	45
Orange	4	7	20

   (a) What percentage of each packet was strawberry flavoured?
   (b) Which packet had the highest proportion of lime-flavoured sweets?
   (c) Which packet had the lowest proportion of orange sweets?

3.3 Working out a percentage of an amount

■ **To work out a percentage of an amount write the percentage
  as a fraction with a denominator of 100. Then multiply the
  fraction by the amount.**

Teaching reference:
(*pp 185–188, sections 14.4,
14.5*)
pp 235–244, sections 14.4,
14.5, 14.6

Example 3
Work out 15% of 40.

Change 15% to a fraction with a denominator of 100 and multiply
it by 40.

$$\frac{15}{100} \times 40 = 6$$

Exercise 3C   Links (*14D, 14E*) 14E, 14F, 14G, 14H

1   Work out
    (a) 5% of 60   (b) 10% of 30   (c) 15% of 70   (d) 25% of 36
    (e) 45% of 80   (f) 10% of £2   (g) 15% of £9   (h) 24% of £10
    (i) 36% of £50   (j) 90% of £145.

2   Peter scored 75% in an English test. The test was marked out of 60. How many marks did Peter score?

3   10% of the students in a class of 30 were absent for a French lesson. How many students were absent?

4   A football club won 86% of the 50 games they played in a season. How many games did they win?

5   A CD player normally costs £80. In a sale it is reduced by 20%.
(a)   How much is the CD player reduced by?
(b)   How much does the CD player cost in the sale?

6   The normal price of a dress is £36. A reduction of 15% is made during a sale. How much does the dress cost in the sale?

3.4 Simplifying ratios

<table>
<tr><td></td><td>Teaching reference: pp 262–266, sections 17.1, 17.2</td></tr>
</table>

■   **A ratio is a way of showing the relationship between two numbers.**

■   **You can simplify a ratio if you can divide its numbers by a common factor.**

Example 4

There are 16 boys and 14 girls in a Year 11 tutor group.
Write down the ratio of boys to girls. Give your answer in its simplest form.

The ratio of boys to girls is $16:14$.
16 and 14 have a common factor of 2.
The ratio can be simplified to $8:7$.

Exercise 3D   **Links** (*17A, 17B*) **17A, 17B**

1   Write these ratios in their simplest form:
(a) $8:4$ (b) $9:3$ (c) $12:4$ (d) $9:6$
(e) $15:9$ (f) $24:16$ (g) $35:21$ (h) $100:30$
(i) $150:100$ (j) $500:250$ (k) $8:4:2$ (l) $10:8:2$
(m) $25:15:5$

Write your answers to questions **2–7** in their simplest form.

2   A bunch of flowers contains 10 daffodils and 15 tulips.
Write down the ratio of daffodils to tulips.

3

Write down the ratio of grey squares to white squares.

4 36 adults and 16 children take a coach trip to Thorpe Park. Write down the ratio of adults to children.

5 Write down the ratio of vowels to consonants in the alphabet.

6 Write down the ratio of face cards to non-face cards in a normal pack of playing cards. (Face cards are King, Queen and Jack.)

7 A box of chocolates contains 20 plain chocolates, 15 milk chocolates and 10 white chocolates. Write down the ratio of the different types of chocolate.

3.5 Ratio, proportion and scale

Teaching reference:
(*pp 217–218, section 17.5*)
pp 270–271, section 17.5

- **Two quantities are in proportion if their ratio stays the same as the quantities get larger or smaller.**

- *Scale* **is the name given to a ratio that shows the relationship between distances or measurements in maps and plans and real distances or measurements.**

Example 5

The ratio of boys to girls in a class is $2:3$. If there are 10 boys in the class, how many girls are there?

Ratio of boys to girls is $2:3$.
There are 10 boys so an equivalent ratio is

$$10:15$$
$$2 \times 5 \qquad 3 \times 5$$

There are 15 girls in the class.

Example 6

A model of a car is made using a scale of $1:50$.
The model is 7 cm long.
How long is the real car?

The ratio $1:50$ means that every cm on the model represents 50 cm on the real car.
So the real car is 7×50 cm long or 350 cm.

Exercise 3E   Links (*17C, 17E*) 17C, 17E

1 The ratio of flour to fat for pastry is $2:1$. If a baker makes some pastry using 300 g of flour how much fat should he use?

2 The instructions on a bottle of orange squash state:

Dilute orange squash with water in the ratio $1:10$.

If a glass of orange drink is made using 30 m*l* of orange squash, how much water should be used?

3   A car uses 5 litres of petrol to travel 30 miles.
     Work out how much petrol will be needed for the car to travel
     180 miles.

4   A cafe owner sells cups of tea and coffee in the ratio of 4 : 5.
     If the cafe owner sells 100 cups of tea one afternoon, work out
     the number of cups of coffee sold.

5   A recipe for 12 cakes requires 120 g of flour.
     Work out the amount of flour required for 30 cakes.

6   A map of a wood is drawn to a scale of 1 : 250.
     On the map the wood is 16 cm wide.
     Write down the width of the real wood.

7   A scale drawing of a classroom is made using a scale of 1 : 20.
     On the drawing the blackboard is 8 cm wide.
     Work out the width of the real blackboard.

8   (a) Write down the actual distance
         from the lighthouse to the port.
     (b) Write down the actual distance
         from the town centre to the port.

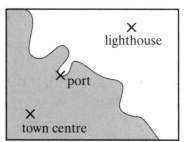

Scale 1 cm = 500 m

Exercise 3F   (Mixed questions)

1   A gardener plants 100 tulips. 35 tulips are red, 42 are yellow
     and the rest are pink.
     (a) What percentage of the tulips are red?
     (b) What percentage of the tulips are pink?

2   Draw a square with sides 10 cm.
     (a) Shade 15% of the square blue.
     (b) Shade 43% of the square red.
     (c) What percentage of the square is left?

3   Kate takes three end-of-term tests in Science. Her scores are
     shown below:

          Biology   13 out of 20
          Chemistry   31 out of 50
          Physics   64 out of 100

     Write down Kate's scores as percentages. Which test did Kate
     do best in?

4   Work out
     (a) 10% of 30   (b) 15% of 60   (c) 18% of 50
     (d) 25% of £6   (e) 30% of £10   (f) 12% of £15.

5 8% of a yogurt is fat. How many grams of fat are there in a yogurt weighing 150 g?

6 The attendance at a football match is 4800. Of the spectators, 26% are women. How many spectators are women?

7 How much will Flash trainers cost in the sale?

> ⩘ **FLASH TRAINERS** ⩘
> Normal Price £45
> **Sale: 20% OFF**
> **NORMAL PRICE**

8 Simplify these ratios:
   (**a**) 8:2   (**b**) 10:5   (**c**) 16:12   (**d**) 50:25
   (**e**) 300:100   (**f**) 500:375   (**g**) 40:16   (**h**) 100:4
   (**i**) 40:20:10   (**j**) 100:50:25

9 A box of chocolates contains 24 plain chocolates and 16 milk chocolates. Write down the ratio of plain chocolates to milk chocolates in its simplest form.

10 A recipe for a cake requires 250 g flour, 125 g fat and 100 g sugar. Write down the ratio of flour to fat to sugar in its simplest form.

11 To make a chilli to serve 4 people, 500 g of mincemeat is needed. How much mincemeat will be needed to serve 18 people?

12 A doll's house is built to a scale of 1:50.
   (**a**) The bed in the doll's house is 4 cm long.
        How long would the real bed be?
   (**b**) A real washing machine is 90 cm high.
        How high would the one in the doll's house be?

Summary of key points

- **Percentage**
    %   ⎫ means 'number of parts per hundred'.
    pc   ⎭

- To write a percentage as a fraction, always use the denominator 100.

- To work out a percentage of an amount write the percentage as a fraction. Then multiply the fraction by the amount.

- A ratio is a way of showing the relationship between two numbers.

- You can simplify a ratio if you can divide its numbers by a common factor.

- Two quantities are in proportion if their ratio stays the same as the quantities get larger or smaller.

- *Scale* is the name given to a ratio that shows the relationship between distances or measurements in maps and plans and real distances or measurements.

4 Algebra – structure and symbols

4.1 Writing expressions

Teaching reference:
(*pp 22–23, section 2.1*)

■ **In algebra, you use letters to represent numbers.**

Example 1

y is a number. Write down an expression for a number which is
(a) 3 less than y (b) 5 times y.

(a) $y - 3$ is a number which is 3 less than y.
($y - 3$ is **not** the same as $3 - y$)
(b) $5y$ is a number which is 5 times y.
($5y$ is short for $5 \times y$)

Example 2

There are c students in a class and g of them are girls. Write down an expression for the number of boys in the class.

You subtract the number of girls from the number of students.
So the number of boys is $c - g$.

Exercise 4A	Links (2A) 2A

Use algebra to write down an expression for each of these numbers:
1 6 less than x. 2 4 more than y. 3 3 times a.
4 c with 7 added. 5 p multiplied by 8. 6 q with 2 subtracted.
7 t more than 9. 8 n less than 5. 9 p times 2.
10 c more than d. 11 m less than n. 12 p multiplied by q.

13 There are b boys and g girls in a class. Write down an expression for the total number of students in the class.

14 The sum of two numbers is 20. One of the numbers is n. Write down an expression for the other number.

15 A cinema ticket costs £5. Write down an expression for the cost, in pounds, of c cinema tickets.

16 x and y are two numbers. Write down an expression for the product of x and y.

17 John's age is y years. Kate is 3 years younger than John. Write down an expression for Kate's age.

18 Write down an expression for the number of days in w weeks.

19 Helen has 10 chocolates. She eats c of them. Write down an expression for the number of chocolates she has left.

20 A box of sweets is shared amongst c children. Each child receives n sweets and there are none left over. Write down an expression for the number of sweets which were in the box.

4.2 Collecting like terms

■ **You can simplify expressions by collecting like terms.**

Teaching reference:
(*pp 24–25, sections 2.3, 2.4*)
pp 29–31, sections 2.2, 2.3, 2.4

Example 3
Simplify

(a) $c + c + c + c$ (b) $8p - 3p$ (c) $5t - 2t + t$

(a) $c + c + c + c = 4c$ (b) $8p - 3p = 5p$ (c) $5t - 2t + t = 4t$

(Remember that t means $1t$.)

Example 4
Simplify

(a) $4a + 5b + 2a + 3b$ (b) $7x + 5 - 4x + 2$ (c) $8p + 2q - 7p - 2q$ (d) $3c + 4d + 5c - 7d$

(a) $4a + 5b + 2a + 3b = 6a + 8b$ (b) $7x + 5 - 4x + 2 = 3x + 7$

(c) $8p + 2q - 7p - 2q = p$ (d) $3c + 4d + 5c - 7d = 8c - 3d$

Example 5
The length of each side of an equilateral triangle is l centimetres. Write down, as simply as possible, an expression for its perimeter.

The perimeter is $l + l + l$.

Expressed as simply as possible, perimeter $= 3l$.

Exercise 4B   **Links (*2B, 2C, 2D*) 2B, 2C, 2D**

Simplify these expressions by collecting like terms:

1 $d + d + d$ **2** $q + q + q + q + q$ **3** $n + n + n + n - n$

4 $7a + 3a$ **5** $8c - 2c$ **6** $5d + d$

7 $9e - 5e$ **8** $5c + 3c + 4c$ **9** $8t - 5t + 2t$

10 $3x + 5x - 7x$ **11** $10h - 2h - 5h$ **12** $5a + 3b + 2a + 6b$

13 $4p + 5q + 2p + 3q$ **14** $3x + 4y + 2x$ **15** $7t + 5 - 3t + 4$

16 $8m + 5n - 2m + 4n$ **17** $5c + 6d - 2c - 3d$ **18** $4p + 3q + 5p - 2q$

19 $5x + 2y + 3x - 2y$ **20** $2a + 7b - 4b + 5c$ **21** $6d + 4e + 2d - 7e$

22 $4y + 3 - 2y - 6$ **23** $9a - 5b + 3b$ **24** $7c + 5d + c - 6d$

25 $6p - 4q - 3p - 2q$ **26** $6 + 5x + 2 - 6x$ **27** $m + 4n - 2m$

28 $3x + 2y + 4x - 3y - y$ **29** $6d + 4e - 5d - 3e - e$ **30** $7 - 3t - 1 - 2t + t$

In questions **31–35**, give your answers as simply as possible.

31 The length of each side of a square is d centimetres. Write down an expression for its perimeter.

32 The length of a rectangle is a centimetres and its width is b centimetres. Write down an expression for its perimeter.

33 The lengths, in centimetres, of the sides of a triangle are $2d + 1$, $4d + 5$ and $3d - 4$. Find an expression for its perimeter.

34 Emma's age is t years. David is 3 times as old as Emma. Write down an expression for the sum of their ages.

35 Mel's height is $7h$ and Patsy's height is $5h$. Write down an expression for the difference in their heights.

4.3 Simplifying products

■ **When you multiply with letters and numbers, leave out the ×
sign.**

■ **If there is a number in the expression, write the number down
first.**

Teaching reference:
(*pp 26–27, sections 2.5, 2.6*)
pp 32–33, sections 2.5, 2.6

Example 6

Write these expressions in a simpler form.

(a) $p \times 2$ (b) $m \times n$ (c) $5 \times a \times b$ (d) $c \times d \times e$

(a) $p \times 2 = 2p$ (b) $m \times n = mn$ (c) $5 \times a \times b = 5ab$ (d) $c \times d \times e = cde$

Example 7

Multiply these expressions and give your answer as simply as possible.

(a) $2p \times 6q$ **(b)** $3d \times 2e \times 5f$

(a) $2 \times 6 = 12$

$2p \times 6q = 12pq$

$p \times q = pq$

(b) $3 \times 2 \times 5 = 30$

$3d \times 2e \times 5f = 30def$

$d \times e \times f = def$

Exercise 4C   **Links (*2E, 2F*) 2E, 2F**

Write these expressions in a simpler form.

1 $c \times 2$ **2** $t \times u$ **3** $8 \times d$ **4** $7 \times f \times g$

5 $5 \times x \times y$ **6** $a \times b \times c$ **7** $p \times q \times r$ **8** $3 \times c \times d \times e$

Multiply these expressions and give your answer as simply as possible.

9 $4x \times 5y$ **10** $7f \times 3g$ **11** $6p \times q$ **12** $8d \times 3$

13 $4 \times 5y$ **14** $m \times 2n$ **15** $7 \times pq$ **16** $3s \times 4t \times 2u$

17 $5a \times 4b \times 3c$ **18** $8d \times 3e \times f$ **19** $6x \times y \times 2z$ **20** $8bc \times 5d$

4.4 Order of operations

Teaching reference:
(*pp 28–29, sections 2.8*)

■ **Always work brackets out first.**

■ **BoDMAS helps you remember the order of operations:**

BoDMAS
Brackets of Divide Multiply Add Subtract

■ **When the signs are the same, you do them in the order they appear.**

Example 8

Find the value of each of these expressions.

(a) $5 \times (6 - 2)$ (b) $(5 \times 6) - 2$ (c) $30 \div 5 + 3$ (d) $48 \div 6 \div 2$

(a) $5 \times (6 - 2) = 5 \times 4$
$\qquad\qquad\quad = 20$

(b) $(5 \times 6) - 2 = 30 - 2$
$\qquad\qquad\quad = 28$

(c) $30 \div 5 + 3 = 6 + 3$
$\qquad\qquad\quad = 9$

(d) $48 \div 6 \div 2 = 8 \div 2$
$\qquad\qquad\quad = 4$

Exercise 4D   Links (*2H*) 2H

Find the value of each of these expressions:

1 $6 \times (4 + 3)$ **2** $6 \times 4 + 3$ **3** $6 + 4 \times 3$

4 $8 - 4 \div 2$ **5** $(8 - 4) \div 2$ **6** $8 - (4 \div 2)$

7 $9 + 5 - 4$ **8** $9 + (5 - 4)$ **9** $10 - 7 - 3$

10 $10 - (7 - 3)$ **11** $10 - 7 + 3$ **12** $(8 - 3) \times 2$

13 $8 - 3 \times 2$ **14** $30 \div 6 \div 5$ **15** $10 - (3 \times 3)$

16 $(10 - 3) \times 3$ **17** $9 + 6 \div 3$ **18** $(9 + 6) \div 3$

19 $(4 + 2) \times (5 - 1)$ **20** $4 + 2 \times 5 - 1$ **21** $28 \div 4 - 3 \times 2$

Copy these expressions and insert brackets to make them correct:

22 $8 - 5 \times 6 = 18$ **23** $7 - 5 - 1 = 3$ **24** $3 \times 5 + 3 \times 2 = 48$

Make these expressions correct by replacing the ∗ with + or − or
× or ÷ and using brackets if you need to:

25 $5 * 2 = 3$ **26** $6 * 3 = 18$ **27** $3 * 2 * 4 = 1$

28 $5 * 2 * 7 = 21$ **29** $5 * 2 * 7 = 17$ **30** $5 * 2 * 7 = 19$

4.5 Expanding brackets

Teaching reference:
(*p 30, section 2.9*)
pp 36–42, section 2.9

■ **When you *expand* brackets, you multiply *every* term inside the
brackets by the term outside.**

Example 9

Expand the brackets in these expressions:

(a) $4(a + b)$ (b) $5(3c - 2)$ (c) $p(q + 6)$ (d) $3f(4g - 5h)$

(a) $4(a+b) = 4 \times a + 4 \times b$
$ = 4a + 4b$

(b) $5(3c-2) = 5 \times 3c - 5 \times 2$
$ = 15c - 10$

(c) $p(q+6) = p \times q + p \times 6$
$ = pq + 6p$

(d) $3f(4g-5h) = 3f \times 4g - 3f \times 5h$
$ = 12fg - 15fh$

With practice, you should be able to write the answer straight down, without the working.

Exercise 4E   Links (2*I*) 2I, 2J, 2K, 2L, 2M, 2N, 2O, 2P, 2Q

Expand the brackets in these expressions:

1 $6(c+d)$	**2** $5(p-q)$	**3** $2(x+3)$	**4** $4(y-2)$
5 $7(3a+2)$	**6** $6(4p-5)$	**7** $5(2c+3d)$	**8** $8(3p-4q)$
9 $a(b+2)$	**10** $c(d-2)$	**11** $x(y+z)$	**12** $p(q-r)$
13 $m(n-1)$	**14** $2(5-x)$	**15** $2f(5g+h)$	**16** $3p(q-4r)$
17 $4x(5y+3z)$	**18** $5b(6c-5)$	**19** $7d(3e+1)$	**20** $8a(3b-2c)$

4.6 Equations

■ **In an equation, a symbol or letter represents an unknown number.**

> Teaching reference:
> (*pp 192–195, section 15.1*)
>
> $4 \times \square + 3 = 11$ and
> $4x + 3 = 11$ are equations.

Example 10

Write these equations using letters:

(a) $\square + 7 = 13$

(b) $3 \times \square - 2 = 19$

> You can use any letter to stand for the number but we usually use x.

(a) The equation is $x + 7 = 13$ (b) The equation is $3x - 2 = 19$

Example 11

Kelly thought of a number.

(a) What number did she think of?
(b) Express this problem as an equation.
(a) $8 \times 6 = 48$
    The number she thought of was 8.
(b) Let x stand for the number she thought of.
    The equation is $6x = 48$.

> I think of a number. When I multiply my number by 6, the answer is 48.

Example 12

Here are two number machines.

number $\longrightarrow$ | Add 3 | $\longrightarrow$ | Multiply by 2 | $\longrightarrow$ 16

(a) Find the number which was put in.   (b) Express this problem as an equation.

(a) $(5+3) \times 2 = 16$ The number which was put in was 5.
(b) Let x stand for the number which was put in.
    The equation is $2(x+3) = 16$.

Exercise 4F   Links (*15A, B, C, D, E, F,*) 15A, B, C, D, E, F

In questions **1–10**, write each equation using a letter.

1 $\square - 7 = 9$ **2** $\square + 3 = 11$ **3** $8 \times \square = 32$

4 $9 + \square = 20$ **5** $7 \times \square - 3 = 32$ **6** $\square \times 3 = 21$

7 $3 \times (\square + 1) = 24$ **8** $\square \times 4 + 5 = 13$

9 $(5 + \square) \times 2 = 16$ **10** $7 + 5 \times \square = 27$

In questions **11–15**:

(a) find the number,   **(b)** express the problem as an equation.

11 Amy thinks of a number and adds 7 to it. The answer is 11.

12 Ben thinks of a number and multiplies it by 5. The answer is 45.

13 Fatima thinks of a number. She adds 2 to it and multiplies the result by 4. The answer is 36.

14 Floyd thinks of a number. He multiplies it by 2 and subtracts 5 from the result. The answer is 12.

15 Dara thinks of a number. She multiplies it by 6 and adds 7 to the result. The answer is 31.

In questions **16–20**:

(a) find the number which was put in,   **(b)** express the problem as an equation.

16   **17**

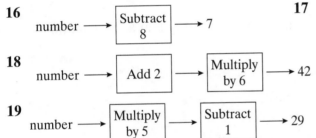

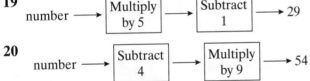

Exercise 4G   Mixed questions

1 Use algebra to write down an expression for a number which is:
    (a) 7 more than p **(b)** 8 times q **(c)** m less than n.

2 Flora's height is h centimetres. She is 7 centimetres taller than Linton. Write down an expression for Linton's height.

3 Simplify these expressions by collecting like terms:
    (a) $y + y + y + y + y + y$ **(b)** $6p - 2p$
    (c) $7q + q - 5q$ **(d)** $6a + 3b + 3a + 4b$
    (e) $6c + 9 + 2c - 4$ **(f)** $5d + 3e - 2d - 3e$
    (g) $6x + 3y - 2x - 5y$ **(h)** $5m - 3n - 2n - m$

4 The lengths of the sides of an isosceles triangle are a, a and b. Write down an expression for its perimeter. Give your answer as simply as possible.

5 Write these expressions in a simpler form:
   (a) $3 \times d$ (b) $m \times n$ (c) $9 \times d \times e$ (d) $b \times c \times d$

6 Multiply these expressions and give your answer as simply as possible:
   (a) $a \times 3b$ (b) $3p \times 4q$ (c) $2m \times 5n$ (d) $2a \times 4b \times 3c$

7 Find the value of each of these expressions:
   (a) $6 \times (3 + 4)$ (b) $6 \times 3 + 4$ (c) $10 - 12 \div 3$

8 Copy these equations and insert brackets to make them correct:
   (a) $6 \times 5 - 3 = 12$ (b) $7 - 2 \times 4 = 20$ (c) $9 - 3 + 2 = 4$

9 Expand the brackets in these expressions:
   (a) $5(x - y)$ (b) $7(2c + 1)$ (c) $p(q + 4)$
   (d) $a(m - n)$ (e) $6d(2e - f)$ (f) $3t(4u + 5)$

10 Write each of these equations using a letter:
   (a) $5 \times \square - 4 = 36$ (b) $7 \times (\square + 1) = 35$ (c) $1 + \square \times 7 = 50$

11 Kerry thinks of a number. She subtracts 4 from it and multiplies the result by 3. The answer is 36.
   (a) What number did she think of?   (b) Express this problem as an equation.

12

number $\longrightarrow$ [Multiply by 6] $\longrightarrow$ [Add 9] $\longrightarrow$ 33

   (a) Find the number which was put in.   (b) Express the problem as an equation.

Summary of key points

- In algebra, you use letters to represent numbers.
- You can simplify expressions by *collecting like terms*.
- When you multiply with letters and numbers, leave out the × sign.
- If there is a number in the expression, write the number down first.
- Always work brackets out first.
- BoDMAS helps you remember the order of operations:

  BoDMAS
  Brackets   of   Divide   Multiply   Add   Subtract

- When the signs are the same, you do them in the order they appear.
- When you *expand* brackets, you multiply *every* term inside the brackets by the term outside.
- In an equation, a symbol or letter represents an unknown number.

5 Algebra – coordinates

5.1 Inequalities

- $a > b$ a is greater than b.
- $x \leqslant y$ x is less than or equal to y.
- There are four signs to use: $> < \geqslant \leqslant$
  Notice that the larger value is at the wide end of the sign.

Example 1
Show $x > -1$ on a number line.

x can be any number greater than -1:

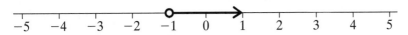

- You do not want -1 included so it is marked by a circle.

Example 2
Show $3 \geqslant x$ on a number line.

x can be any number less than 3 as well as 3.

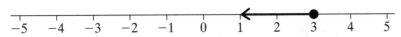

- You want 3 included so it is a solid spot.

Example 3
Write down as an inequality the set of points shown on this number line:

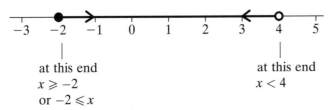

at this end   at this end
$x \geqslant -2$ $x < 4$
or $-2 \leqslant x$

These two inequalities can be combined into the single result
$$-2 \leqslant x < 4$$

Exercise 5A   **Links 21N**

---

1   Draw a separate number line to mark each of these inequalities:
   - **(a)** $x > 2$
   - **(b)** $x < -2$
   - **(c)** $x \leqslant 0$
   - **(d)** $x \geqslant -1$
   - **(e)** $x > -5$
   - **(f)** $x \leqslant 4$
   - **(g)** $3 < x$
   - **(h)** $-2 > x$
   - **(i)** $5 \leqslant x$
   - **(j)** $-3 \geqslant x$

2   In the following questions put in the correct sign:
   (a) $4 * 7$ **(b)** $-15 * -9$
   (c) $3 * -11$ **(d)** $-23 * -27$
   (e) $(2+3) * (5-1)$ **(f)** $(-2+3) * (2-3)$
   (g) $(15-4) * (3-14)$ **(h)** $(0-6) * (0-15)$

3   Write down the inequalities represented by the diagrams:
   (a)

   ```
   ──┬──○───────→
   -3  -2  -1   0   1   2   3
   ```

   (b)

   ```
   ──┬──┬──←───────●──┬──
   -3  -2  -1   0   1   2   3
   ```

   (c)

   ```
   ←─────○──┬──┬──┬──┬──
   -3  -2  -1   0   1   2   3
   ```

   (d)

   ```
   ──┬──┬──┬──●───────→
   -3  -2  -1   0   1   2   3
   ```

4   Use separate number lines to show these inequalities:
   (a) $-2 < x < 3$
   (b) $-5 \leqslant x \leqslant -2$
   (c) $1 < x \leqslant 4$
   (d) $-3 \leqslant x < 2$

5   Write down the inequalities shown on the number lines:
   (a)

   ```
   ──┬──┬──●──→    ←──●──┬──┬──┬──┬──
   -5  -4  -3  -2  -1   0   1   2   3   4
   ```

   (b)

   ```
   ──┬──○──×←──●──┬──┬──┬──┬──┬──┬──
   -5  -4  -3  -2  -1   0   1   2   3   4
   ```

   (c)

   ```
   ──┬──┬──┬──┬──┬──○──→    ←──○──
   -5  -4  -3  -2  -1   0   1   2   3   4
   ```

5.2   Read and plot coordinates in the first quadrant

Teaching reference:
(*pp 116–117, section 9.1*)
pp 137–139, section 9.1

■   **Coordinates are 'across the floor' and 'up the wall'.**
   $(3, 2)$ means 3 across and 2 up.

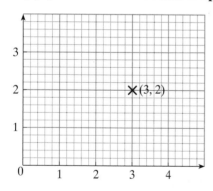

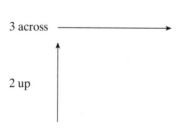

3 across ──────────────→

2 up

Exercise 5B   **Links (*9A, 9B*) 9A, 9B, 9C**

1   Write down the coordinates of the points marked on the
graph:

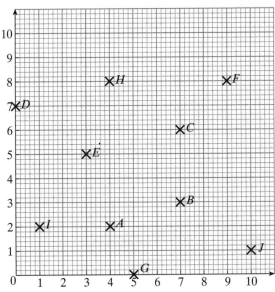

2   Plot the following points on a grid. The grid needs to go up to
10 in each direction.

A (4, 3); *B* (2, 6); *C* (0, 4); *D* (7, 0); *E* (8, 1); *F* (3, 9); *G* (8, 7); *H* (5, 2).

5.3 Read and plot coordinates in all four quadrants

Teaching reference:
(*p 126, section 9.5*)
pp 150–156, section 9.5

■   The *x*- and *y*-axes can both be extended to include negative
numbers. Coordinates can include positive and negative
numbers.

Example 4

What are the coordinates of the points *A*, *B* and *C* on the grid?

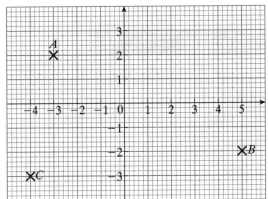

A is (−3, 2); *B* is (5, −2); *C* is (−4, −3).

1   Write down the coordinates of the points marked on the grid.

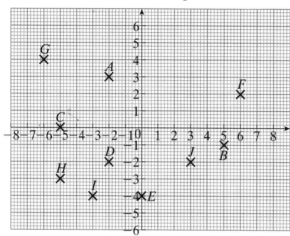

2   Plot the following points on a grid. The grid needs to go from −6 to +6 in each direction.

    A (−3, 0); *B* (−4, 5); *C* (5, −4); *D* (−4, −5); *E* (3, −3); *F* (−2, 6); *G* (−3, −1); *H* (0, −5).

5.4 1-D, 2-D or 3-D?

Teaching reference: pp 157–158, section 9.6

■   **The number line goes in one direction. This is called one-dimensional (1-D for short).**

■   **The coordinates in the exercises were reached by going in two directions. This covers a flat shape which is two-dimensional (2-D for short).**

■   **Solid shapes and space are three-dimensional. Volumes are three-dimensional (3-D for short). To describe positions in space a third, *z*-axis is used. These coordinates look like (1, 2, 3).**

1   Separate these shapes into those which are two-dimensional (flat) and those which are three-dimensional:

    Pentagon, pyramid, hexagon, triangle, cylinder, cone, trapezium, cuboid, rectangle, sphere, square, circle.

2   Make a list of the three-dimensional coordinates from the following:

    (1, 4, 2), (3, 3), (6, 2, 1, 4), (0, 3), (2, 3, 4), (4, 5, 0), (6, 0, 7), (6, 3), (3), (−3, 0, 0).

3

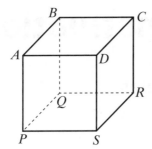

Say whether the shape made by the (lettered) points is 1-D, 2-D or 3-D:

(a) *AB*   (b) *ABC*
(c) *ABCD*   (d) *PR*
(e) *PABC*   (f) *PSB*
(g) *PQDA*   (h) *PQRSC*
(i) *PC*   (j) *PCR*

Summary of key points

- $a > b$ *a* is greater than *b*.

- $x \leqslant y$ *x* is less than or equal to *y*.

- **There are four signs to use:** $> \; < \; \geqslant \; \leqslant$
  Notice that the larger value is at the wide end of the sign.

- **Coordinates are 'across the floor' and 'up the wall'.**
  (3, 2) means 3 across and 2 up.

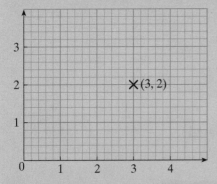

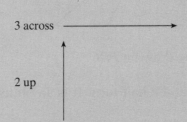

- **The *x*- and *y*-axes can both be extended to include negative numbers. Coordinates can include positive and negative numbers.**

- **The number line goes in one direction.**
  This is called one-dimensional (1-D for short).

- **Flat shapes are two-dimensional (2-D for short).**

- **Solid shapes, space and volumes are three-dimensional (3-D for short).**
  To describe positions in space a third, *z*-axis is used.
  These coordinates look like (1, 2, 3).

6 Angles and construction

6.1 Right, acute and obtuse angles

Teaching reference:
(*pp 41–43, sections 3.2, 3.3*)
pp 50–52, sections 3.2, 3.3

- An angle which is a quarter turn is called a *right angle*.
- An angle which is less than a quarter turn is called an *acute angle*.
- An angle which is more than a quarter turn but less than a half turn is called an *obtuse angle*.
- This diagram shows angle *ABC*. The angle is described as it is drawn.

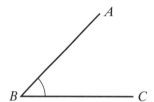

Example 1

Write down the mathematical name for the type of angle marked and use letters to describe the angle.

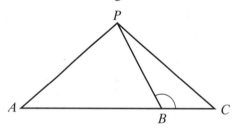

The marked angle is made by drawing *PBC*.
It is named angle *PBC*.
It is between a quarter turn and a half turn. It is an obtuse angle.

Exercise 6A   Links (*3B, 3C*) 3B, 3C

In each question use letters to describe the marked angle and also say whether it is acute or obtuse.

1

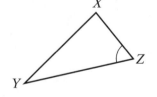

2

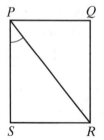

3

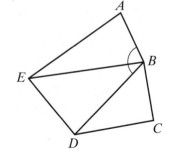

4

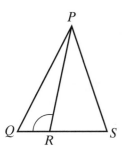

5

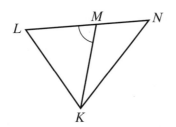

6

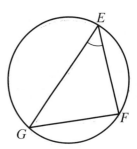

■   **An angle which is more than a half turn is called a *reflex angle*.**

Example 2

Use letters to describe the angles marked at *A* and *C*:
The angle at *A* is angle *DAB*. It is an obtuse angle.

The marked angle at *C* is a reflex angle. There is also an obtuse angle at *C*. To avoid confusion the marked angle is described as reflex angle *DCB*.

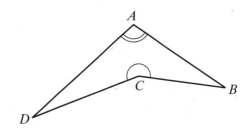

Example 3

Copy the diagram below and mark angle *C*, angle *APB* and angle *PBC*.
(Note: the full description of angle *C* is angle *PCB*. You can use the single letter if there is only one angle at the point.)

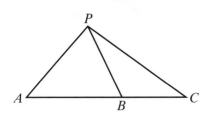

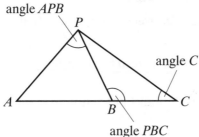

Exercise 6B   **Links (3C) 3C**

In each question, copy the diagram and mark the named angles.

1

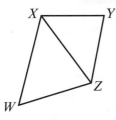

Angle *W*, angle *YXZ* and angle *XZW*

2

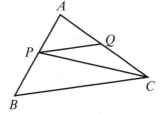

Angle *B*, angle *AQP* and angle *APC*

3

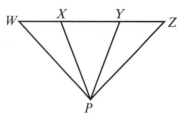

Angle *PXY*, angle *ZPY* and angle *WYP*

4

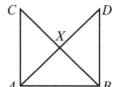

Angle *C*, angle *AXB* and angle *CBA*

5

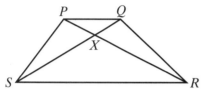

Angle *SPQ* and reflex angle *SXR*

6

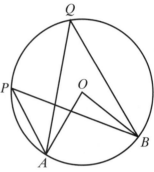

Reflex angle *AOB*, angle *PAQ* and angle QBP.

6.2 Parallel and perpendicular

Teaching reference:
pp 50–51, section 3.2

- **Lines which have a right angle between them are called** *perpendicular lines*.

- **Lines which stay the same distance apart are called** *parallel lines*.

These marks are used to show parallel and perpendicular lines.

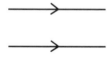   

Exercise 6C   **Links (3***I***) 3I**

1   Name lines that are:
(**a**) parallel   (**b**) perpendicular.

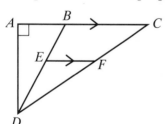

2   Name lines that are:
(**a**) parallel   (**b**) perpendicular.

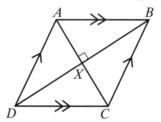

3   The shape shown right is a cuboid.
  (a) Name a line that is parallel to *AB*.
  (b) Name a line that is parallel to *BD*.
  (c) Name a line that is perpendicular to *BD*.
  (d) Name a line that is perpendicular to *AD*.
  (e) Name a plane that is parallel to *SRCD*.
  (f) Name a plane that is perpendicular to *ACRP*.

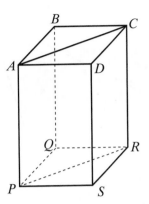

6.3 Measuring, drawing and estimating angles

Teaching reference:
pp 43–45, sections 3.4, 3.5
pp 52–55, sections 3.4, 3.5

Example 4
Measure the angle shown in the diagram.

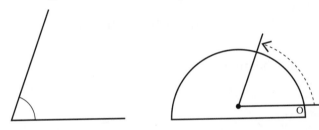

You are turning anticlockwise from O. This is the inside scale. The angle is 70°.

Exercise 6D   **Links (*3B, 3D, 3E*) 3D, 3E**

---

1   Measure the angles in the diagrams:

  (a)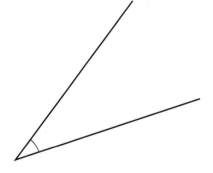

  (b)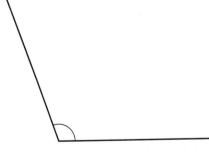

(c)

(d)

(e)

(f)

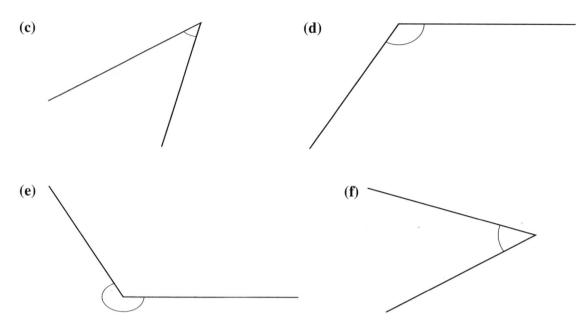

2 Use a ruler and protractor to draw these angles.
Do a separate diagram for each answer.
(a) 25° **(b)** 80° **(c)** 115° **(d)** 215° **(e)** 320° **(f)** 155°

3 Estimate the size of these angles.
Check your answers by measuring (no cheating!).
(a) **(b)** **(c)**

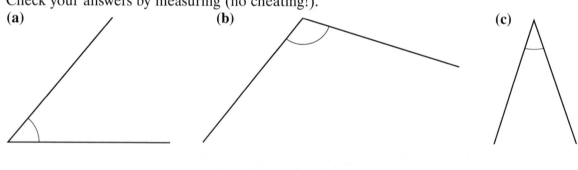

(d) **(e)**

Activity (in pairs)
Draw an angle. Each person estimates the size and writes down
their estimate.
Measure the angle. The person who is closest wins.
A full game is a set of 9.

6.4 Constructions

Example 5

Construct a triangle with angle $A = 40°$, angle $B = 50°$ and
$AB = 6$ cm.

It is best to draw the length first.

Then draw the angles at each end.

Then complete the triangle.

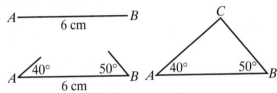

(A sketch to see the general shape helps to make sure your triangle
stays on the paper.)

1 Measure these lines to the nearest mm:

   (a) ————————————

   (b) ——————

   (c) ———————————————

   (d) —————

   (e) ——————————————————

2 Draw lines with length

   (a) 32 mm   (b) 57 mm   (c) 44 mm

   (d) 61 mm   (e) 87 mm

3 Use a ruler and protractor to construct these triangles as
accurately as possible. Measure and write down the length of
the other side(s) and angle(s).

   (a) 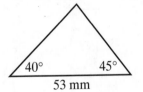   (b) 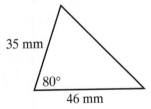   (c)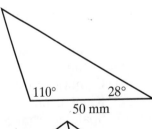

   (d) 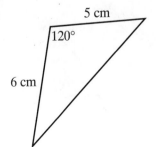   (e) 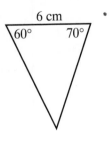   (f)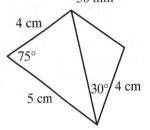

6.5 Bearings

■ **A bearing is an angle measured from facing North and turning clockwise. It is always a three-figure number.**

Example 6

Find the bearing of *A* from *B*.

'From *B*' tells me that I am at *B* and facing North.

The bearing is how far I have to turn to face *A*.

I turn clockwise.

The angle is 57°.

I make this three figures by calling it 057°.

The bearing of *A* from *B* is 057°.

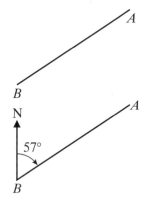

Exercise 6F   **Links 3J**

1   Measure and write down the bearing of:
    (a) *A* from *B*   **(b)** *B* from *A*.

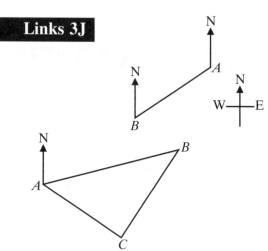

2   Measure and write down the bearing of:
    (a) *B* from *C*   **(b)** *C* from *A*
    (c) *A* from *B*   **(d)** *B* from *A*.

3   Using the map of East Anglia find the bearing of
    (a) Great Yarmouth from Norwich
    (b) Colchester from London
    (c) Cambridge from Luton
    (d) Cambridge from Kings Lynn
    (e) Spalding from Kings Lynn
    (f) Boston from Norwich
    (g) Ipswich from Bury St. Edmunds
    (h) Southend from Boston.

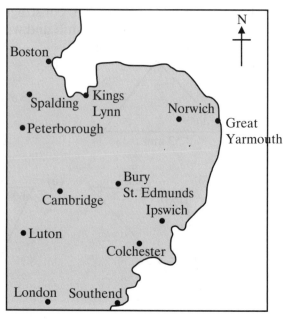

Exercise 6G   Mixed questions

1 Give the mathematical type and describe with letters the marked angles:

(a)

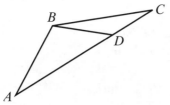

(b)

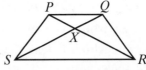

(c)

2 Copy the diagrams and mark on them the angles asked for:

(a)

Angle *C*, angle *CBD* and angle *BDA*

(b)

Reflex angle *QXR*, angle *XSP* and angle *PQS*

3

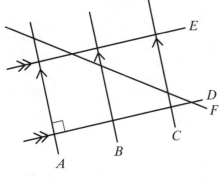

(a) List sets of lines which are parallel.
(b) List pairs of lines which are perpendicular.

4 Use a ruler and protractor to draw these diagrams as accurately as possible. Measure all remaining sides and angles.

(a)

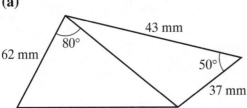

43 mm
80°
62 mm
50°
37 mm

(b)

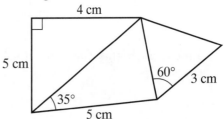

4 cm
5 cm
60°
3 cm
35°
5 cm

5

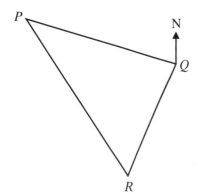

Find the bearing of
(a) R from Q
(b) P from Q
(c) R from P.

Summary of key points

- An angle which is a quarter turn is called a *right angle*.
- An angle which is less than a quarter turn is called an *acute angle*.
- An angle which is more than a quarter turn but less than a half turn is called an *obtuse angle*.
- This angle is described as angle *ABC:*

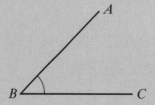

- An angle which is more than a half turn is called a *reflex angle*.
- Lines which have a right angle between them are called *perpendicular lines*.

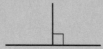

- Lines which stay the same distance apart are called *parallel lines*.

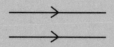

- A bearing is an angle measured from facing North and turning clockwise. It is always a three-figure number.

7 Quadrilaterals and circles

7.1 Quadrilaterals

■ **A quadrilateral is a four-sided shape.**

You need to know these quadrilaterals and their properties:

Name	Shape	Properties
Trapezium		1 pair of parallel sides
Parallelogram		2 pairs of parallel sides opposite sides equal opposite angles equal
Rhombus		2 pairs of parallel sides all sides equal diagonals cross at right angles
Rectangle		all angles 90° opposite sides equal opposite sides parallel diagonals equal
Square		All angles 90° all sides equal opposite sides parallel diagonals equal and cross at right angles
Arrowhead		2 pairs of adjacent sides of the same length
Kite		2 equal pairs of adjacent sides (next to each other) 1 equal pair of opposite angles diagonals cross at 90°

Example 1

Complete the sentence with:
equal, parallel, opposite, sides, angles, 90, 180.

A rhombus has 4 equal _____; the diagonals cross at _____ degrees.

A rhombus has 4 equal <u>sides</u>; the diagonals cross at <u>90</u> degrees.

Example 2

Name these special quadrilaterals:

(a)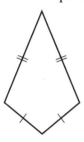

(b)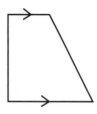

(a) Kite.

(b) Trapezium.

Example 3

On squared paper draw:

(a) a trapezium with parallel sides 5 cm and 3 cm

(b) a square of side 4 cm.

(a) (b)

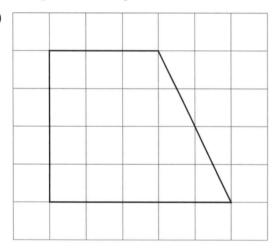

1 Complete the sentences using numbers and words chosen from:
   equal, parallel, opposite, sides, angles, 4, 90.
   (a) Opposite _____ of a square are _____, all sides are _____.
   (b) A quadrilateral is a _____ sided shape.
   (c) _____ sides of a rectangle are _____ and _____.
   (d) The diagonals of a kite cross at _____ degrees.
   (e) Opposite sides of a rhombus are _____ and all _____
   are _____, the diagonals cross at _____ degrees.
   (f) A trapezium has _____ sides.
   (g) _____ sides of a parallelogram are _____ and _____.

2 Name these special quadrilaterals:

(a)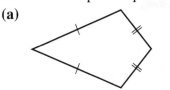

(b)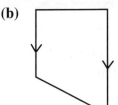

(c)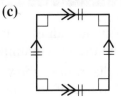

(d)

(e)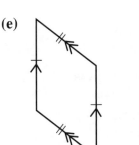

(f)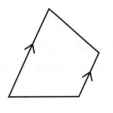

(g)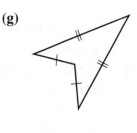

3 On squared paper draw
  (a) a parallelogram with longest side 6 cm
  (b) a rhombus with side 4 cm
  (c) a trapezium with parallel sides 3 cm and 7 cm
  (d) a rectangle with opposite sides 2 cm and 5 cm
  (e) a kite with adjacent sides 4 cm and 6 cm
  (f) an arrowhead with two pairs of sides 6 cm and 4 cm.

7.2 Circles

Teaching reference:
(*p 233, section 19.1*)
pp 286–288, section 19.1

■ **A circle is the shape enclosed by a curve which is everywhere the same distance from the centre.**

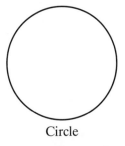

Circle Circle and centre Circle and radius

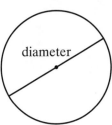

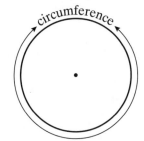

Circle and diameter

Circle and circumference

■ **The circumference of a circle is the distance measured around the curve which makes the circle.**

Exercise 7B   **Links** (*19D, 19E, 19F*) **19E, 19F, 19G**

1   Draw a circle radius 5 cm.
    Label the radius, circumference and diameter.
2   Draw a diagram to show the radius, diameter and
    circumference of a circle.

Summary of key points

- A quadrilateral is a four-sided shape.
- A circle is the shape enclosed by a curve which is
  everywhere the same distance from the centre.
- The circumference of a circle is the distance measured
  around the curve which makes the circle.

8 Symmetry and transformations

8.1 Reflective symmetry in 2-D shapes

Teaching reference:
(*pp 220–223, sections 18.1, 18.2*)

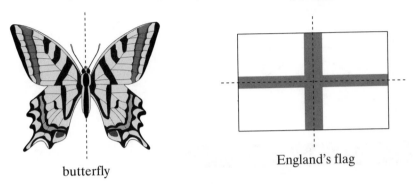

butterfly

England's flag

- ■ A line of symmetry is sometimes called a *mirror line*.

- ■ A 2-D shape has a line of symmetry if the line divides the shape into two halves and one half is the mirror image of the other half.

Example 1

Half of a symmetrical shape is shown here.
The dotted line is the mirror line. Copy and complete the shape.

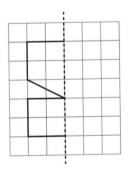

Mark each corner (vertex) with a dot.
Each dot has an image the same distance from the mirror line but on the other side.

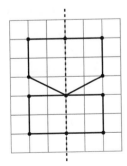

Example 2

Draw in all lines of symmetry for these shapes:

(a)

(b)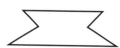

(a)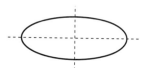

(b)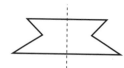

Exercise 8A   **Links** (*18A, 18B*) **18A**

1 Half a symmetrical shape is shown. The dotted line is the mirror line. Copy and complete each shape.

(a) 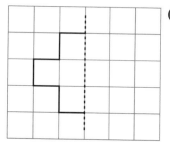   (b) 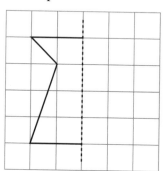   (c)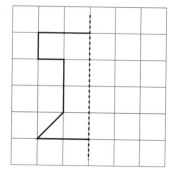

2 Copy and draw in all the lines of symmetry for these shapes:

(a) 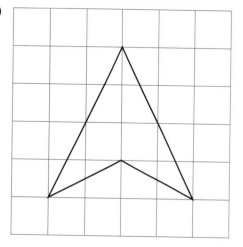   (b)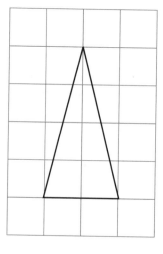

(c)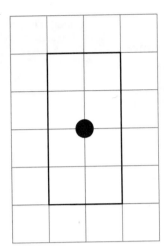

(d)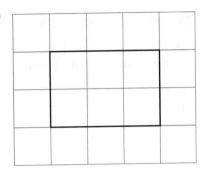

(e)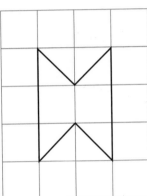

(f)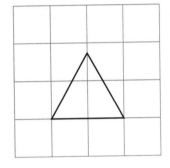

3 Copy and draw in the lines of symmetry for these figures:
8, 3, 4, 10, 5

4 Copy each design and draw in the lines of symmetry:

(a)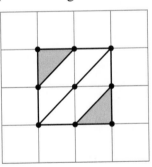

(b)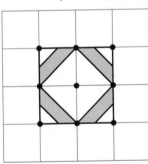

(c)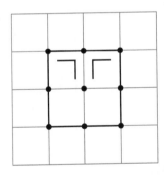

(d)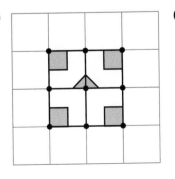

(e)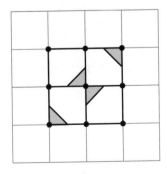

(f)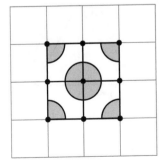

8.2 Rotational symmetry

Teaching reference:
(*pp 224–225, sections 18.3*)
pp 277–278, sections 18.3,
18.4

■ **A 2-D shape with rotational symmetry repeats the appearance of its starting position two or more times during a full turn.**

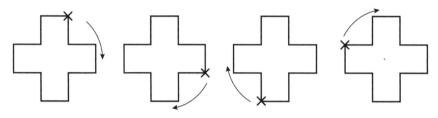

A cross looks the same four times during a full turn.

■ **The order of rotational symmetry is the number of times the original appearance is repeated in a full turn.**

The order of rotational symmetry of the cross is 4.

Example 3

Write down the order of rotational symmetry of these shapes:

(a)

(b)

(c)

(d)

(a)

(b)

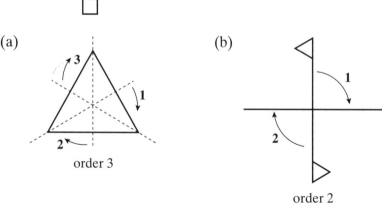

order 3

order 2

(c)

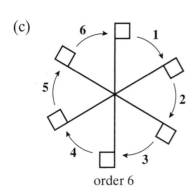

order 6

(d)

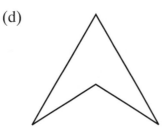

No rotational symmetry as it is not in the same position until it completes a whole turn.

■ **Regular polygons have the same number of lines of symmetry as they have sides.**

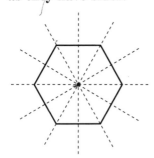

Hexagon (6 sides)
6 lines of symmetry
Rotational symmetry order 6

■ **The order of rotational symmetry of a regular polygon is the same as the number of sides.**

Exercise 8B   **Links** (*18C, 18D*) **18C, 18D**

You may find tracing paper helpful in this exercise.
1   Write down the order of rotational symmetry of these shapes:

(a)

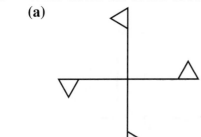

(b)

(c)

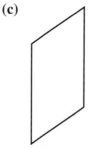

(d)

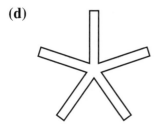

(e)

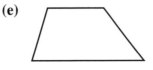

(f)

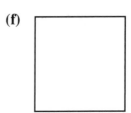

2 Write down the order of rotational symmetry for each of these polygons:

(a)  **(b)**  **(c)**  **(d)**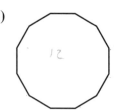

8.3 Rotation

- **Images of a shape which are formed by turning are called *rotations* of the shape.**

- **The point about which turning occurs is called the *centre of rotation*.**

Teaching reference:
(*pp 280–282, section 22.2*)
pp 344–346, section 22.2

Example 4

Draw the image of the shape after it has been rotated

(a) $\frac{1}{4}$ turn clockwise about A

(b) $\frac{1}{2}$ turn about A.

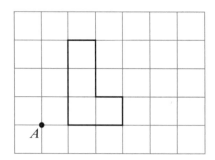

Use tracing paper to help you.

(a)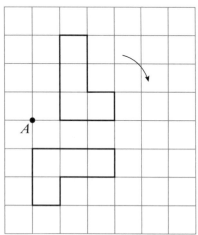

(b)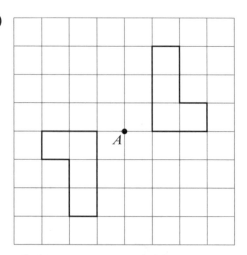

Note:
$\frac{1}{2}$ turn anticlockwise is the same as $\frac{1}{2}$ turn clockwise.

Example 5

Describe fully the transformation which maps triangle A onto triangle B:

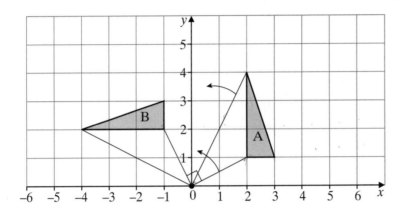

Notice each point/line moves 90° anticlockwise.

Anticlockwise rotation 90°
Centre (0, 0)
Notice the shape remains exactly the same in lengths and angles.

Example 6

Rotate the shape below about the centre through

(a) $\frac{1}{4}$ turn anticlockwise (call it A)

(b) $\frac{1}{2}$ turn anticlockwise (call it B)

(c) $\frac{3}{4}$ turn anticlockwise (call it C).

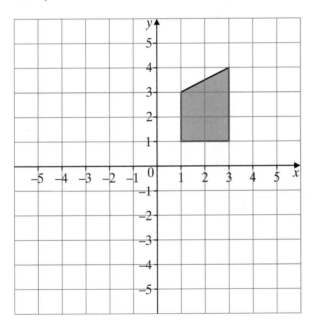

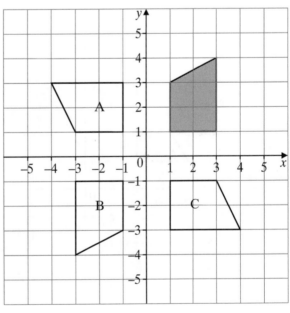

Exercise 8C   Links (22B) 22B

1 Copy these shapes and draw the image after an anticlockwise rotation of 90° about each of the centres marked:

(a)

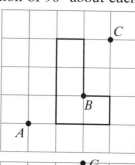

(b)

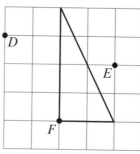

(c)

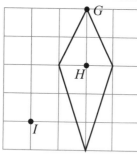

(d)

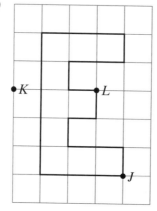

2 Describe fully the transformation which maps triangle A onto B, C, and D respectively.

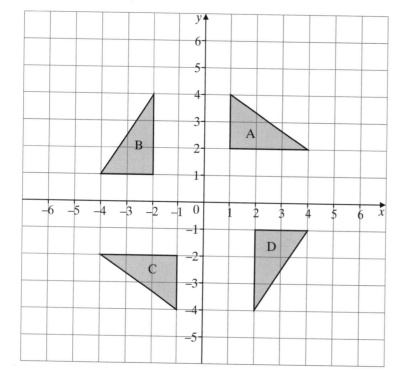

3 Copy each diagram and rotate each shape about $(0,0)$
   (i) 90° clockwise
   (ii) 270° clockwise.

(a)

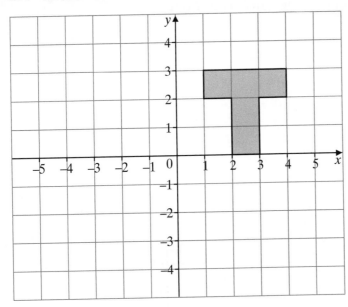

(b)

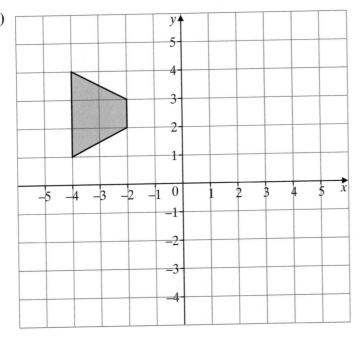

8.4 Reflection

- **Mathematical reflections have images which are the same distance behind the mirror line as the object is in front.**

Teaching reference:
(*pp 282–284, section 22.3*)
pp 346–348, section 22.3

Example 7

Reflect the shape in the mirror line:

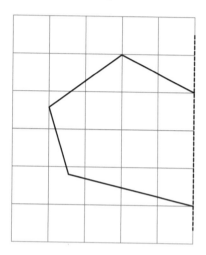 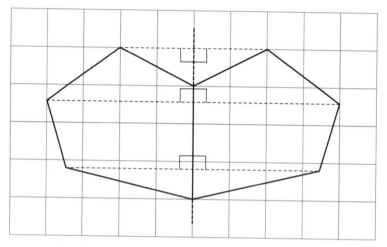

The image is the same distance on the other side measured at right angles to the mirror line.

- **Mirror lines are two-way. The mirror line may go through the object requiring reflections to go both ways.**

Example 8

Reflect the shape in the mirror line:

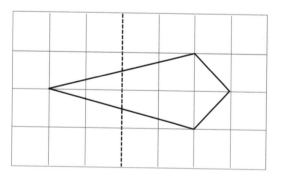 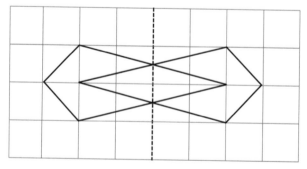

1   Copy each shape. Draw the image of the reflection in the mirror line (dotted).

(a)

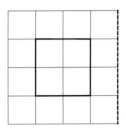

(b)

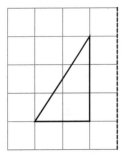

(c)

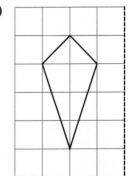

(d)

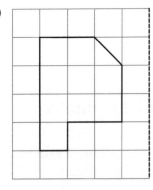

(e)

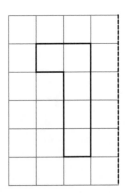

(f)

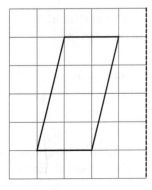

(g)

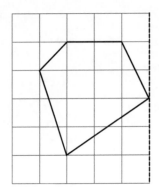

(h)

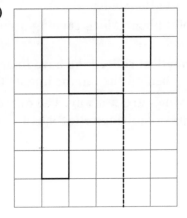

(i)

(j)

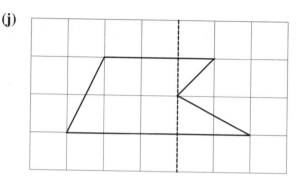

Summary of key points

- A line of symmetry is sometimes called a *mirror line*.

- A 2-D shape has a line of symmetry if the line divides the shape into 2 halves and one half is the mirror image of the other half.

- A 2-D shape with rotational symmetry repeats the appearance of its starting position two or more times during a full turn.

- The order of rotational symmetry is the number of times the original appearance is repeated in a full turn.

- Regular polygons have the same number of lines of symmetry as they have sides.

- The order of rotational symmetry of a regular polygon is the same as the number of sides.

- Images of a shape which are formed by turning are called *rotations* of the shape.

- The point about which turning occurs is called the *centre of rotation*.

- Mathematical reflections have images which are the same distance behind the mirror line as the object is in front.

- Mirror lines are two-way. The mirror line may go through the object requiring reflections to go both ways.

9 Scale and conversions

9.1 Time – reading time from digital and analogue clocks, using am, pm and 24-hour clock times

Teaching reference: pp 115–118, section 7.6

Exercise 9A   **Links** *(7F, 7G, 7H)* **7F, 7G, 7H**

1   Write down the times shown by these clocks as you would say them:

(a) 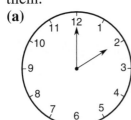   **(b)** 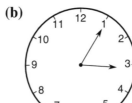   **(c)**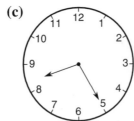

(d) 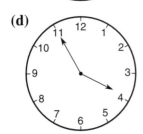   **(e)** 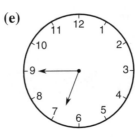   **(f)**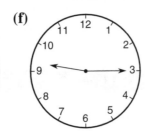

2   Draw clock faces and mark on them:
(a) eight o'clock
(b) five minutes to six
(c) a quarter past five
(d) half past seven
(e) a quarter to twelve
(f) ten minutes past four.

3   Write these times as you would say them:
(a) 4:30   (b) 10:05   (c) 3:15
(d) 7:45   (e) 12:35   (f) 8:50

4   Write these times as they would appear on a digital display:
(a) two o'clock
(b) five past three
(c) a quarter past eight
(d) half past midnight
(e) twenty to seven
(f) five to three.

5 Change these times to 24-hour clock times:
  (a) 2:15 am
  (b) 3:20 pm
  (c) 12:40 pm
  (d) 11:30 pm
  (e) 9:55 am
  (f) three forty five pm
  (g) ten past eight am
  (h) seven fifty pm
  (i) twenty to ten pm
  (j) ten past midnight.

6 Write these 24-hour clock times as 12-hour clock times
  (am or pm):
  (a) 1520 **(b)** 0715 **(c)** 2330 **(d)** 1230 **(e)** 1845
  (f) 1005 **(g)** 1920 **(h)** 1350 **(i)** 2020 **(j)** 0325

9.2 Reading scales

There is rarely room to number all the marks on a scale. Scales do
not always go up in 1s. Sometimes they go up in 2s or 5s or
something else.

Teaching reference:
(*pp 100–103, section 7.7*)
pp 118–122, section 7.7

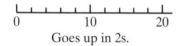

Goes up in 2s.

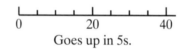

Goes up in 5s.

Exercise 9B   **Links (*7I, 7J, 7K, 7L*) 7I, 7J, 7K, 7L**

1 Give the readings on these scales:
  (a)

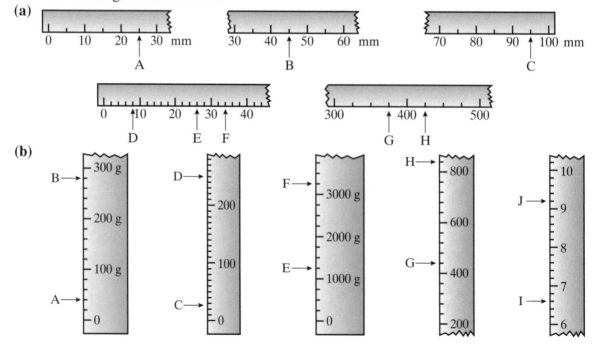

(c)

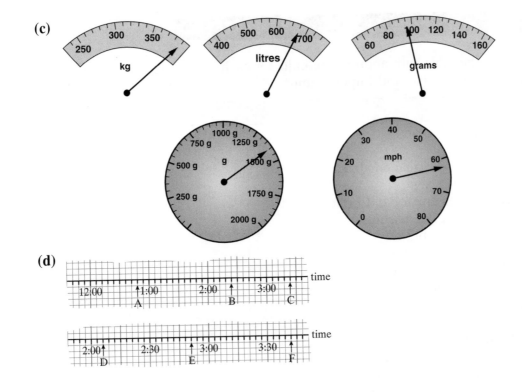

(d)

9.3 Choosing suitable units

■ **Length**
metric: kilometres (km), metres (m), centimetres (cm), millimetres (mm).
Imperial: miles (mi), yards, feet (ft), inches (in).

■ **Weight**
metric: tonnes (t), kilograms (kg), grams (g), milligrams (mg).
Imperial: tons, hundredweight (cwt), stones, pounds (lb), ounces (oz).

■ **Capacity**
metric: litres (*l*), centilitres (c*l*), millilitres (m*l*).
Imperial: gallons, pints (pt).

Example 1

Choose suitable units for

(a) the length of a tennis court   (b) the weight of a blackbird   (c) the capacity of a cup.

(a) Length can be mm, cm, m or km.
A tennis court is nowhere near 1 km long.
mm and cm are too small.
Metres is the sensible unit to use.

(b) The weight of a blackbird must be much less than 1 kg.
Grams are the sensible unit to use.

(c) You cannot get a litre of water into a cup.
Millilitres are the sensible unit to use.

Exercise 9C   Links (*7E*) 7E

Copy and complete the table with appropriate units for each
measurement. Give both metric and Imperial units.

	Metric	Imperial
1 The weight of an exercise book.		
2 The height of a tree.		
3 The length of a window cleaner's ladder.		
4 The capacity of a milk jug.		
5 The distance between Bristol and London.		
6 The weight of a packet of biscuits.		
7 The capacity of a water butt.		
8 The weight of a hippopotamus.		
9 The time taken to run 200 metres.		
10 The height of a daffodil.		
11 The thickness of a pane of glass.		
12 The weight of a person.		
13 The time it takes to walk 20 miles.		
14 The capacity of a can of soft drink.		
15 The time it takes to grow a tomato plant.		
16 The length of a corridor in a school.		
17 The time it takes to boil an egg.		
18 The weight of a sack of coal.		
19 The weight of iron in a portion of breakfast cereal.		
20 The time for a tree to grow to maturity.		

9.4 Estimating

When estimating try to compare the item with a measurement you
know.

> 1 cm is about the width of a fingernail.
> 2 m is the height of a standard door.
> 1 kg is the weight of the usual size bag of sugar.
> 165 ml is about a cupful.

Exercise 9D   Links (*7A*) 7A

Use the picture at the top of the next page to help you make a
sensible estimate for each of the following:

1   The length of the whiteboard.

2   The height of the teacher's desk.

3   The height of the filing cabinet.

4   The thickness of the text book.

5	The length of the board rubber.	6	The height of the seat of the chair.
7	The width of the wallet file.	8	The height of the whiteboard.

Exercise 9E   Links (*7C*) 7C

Put these sets of three in order of weight.
Put the smallest first. Choose the most suitable weight from the list
for each.

1	Canary, crow, swan.	5 g, 50 g, 0.5 kg, 5 kg, 50 kg
2	Labrador, Corgi, St Bernard.	600 g, 6 kg, 20 kg, 60 kg, 200 kg
3	Elephant, bear, wolf.	2000 g, 20 kg, 100 kg, 1000 kg, 4000 kg
4	Shark, whale, goldfish.	800 g, 8 kg, 80 kg, 250 kg, 800 kg, 8000 kg
5	Pig, horse, sheep.	20 kg, 80 kg, 200 kg

Exercise 9F   Links (*7B*) 7B

Use the picture to help you estimate the capacity of each of the
following:

1 The watering can.

2 The flower pot.

3 The water butt.

4 The bucket.

5 The wheelbarrow.

6 The swimming pool.

7 The weedkiller spray.

8 The small bottle (root hormone).

9.5 Converting between metric units

■ **You need to know that:**

Length	Weight	Capacity
10 mm = 1 cm 100 cm = 1 m 1000 mm = 1 m 1000 m = 1 km	1000 mg = 1 g 1000 g = 1 kg 1000 kg = 1 tonne	100 c*l* = 1 litre 1000 m*l* = 1 litre 1000 *l* = 1 cubic metre

You need to remember:

■ **When you change from small units to large units you divide.**

■ **When you change from large units to small units you multiply.**

Example 2

Convert

(i)   0.062 m into cm.

(ii) 23 200 g into kg.

(i)   Centimetres are smaller than metres so you get more of them.
      100 cm = 1 m
      0.062 m = 0.062 × 100 = 6.2 cm

(ii) Kilograms are larger than grams so you get less of them
      1000 g = 1 kg
      23 200 g = 23 200 ÷ 1000 = 23.2 kg

Exercise 9G Links (*13A, 13B, 13C, 13D*) 13A, 13B, 13C, 13D

1 Convert these measurements into mm:
   3 cm   8 cm   2.9 cm   4.7 cm   5.26 cm   6.21 cm

2 Convert into cm:
   129 mm   630 mm   2 m   3.47 m   0.021 km

3 Convert these measurements into grams:
   3 kg   4.1 kg   2.97 kg   0.132 kg   0.0057 kg   230 mg
   8000 mg   7550 mg

4 Convert these amounts to kg:
   15 000 g   6500 g   2 t   3.72 t   0.013 t   20 000 mg
   1 million milligrams

5 Convert these measurements into m*l*:
   5 litres   22.6 litres   3.712 litres   50 c*l*   26 c*l*   200 c*l*

6 Convert these measurements into litres:
   23 000 m*l*   3700 m*l*   500 c*l*   632 c*l*   10 500 c*l*   500 m*l*   850 m*l*

Summary of key points

- **Length**
  metric: **kilometres (km), metres (m), centimetres (cm), millimetres (mm).**
  Imperial: **miles (mi), yards, feet (ft), inches (in).**

- **Weight**
  metric: **tonnes (t), kilograms (kg), grams (g), milligrams (mg).**
  Imperial: **tons, hundredweight (cwt), stones, pounds (lb), ounces (oz).**

- **Capacity**
  metric: **litres (*l*), centilitres (c*l*), millilitres (m*l*).**
  Imperial: **gallons, pints (pt).**

Length	Weight	Capacity
10 mm = 1 cm 100 cm = 1 m 1000 mm = 1 m 1000 m = 1 km	1000 mg = 1 g 1000 g = 1 kg 1000 kg = 1 tonne	100 c*l* = 1 litre 1000 m*l* = 1 litre 1000 *l* = 1 cubic metre

- **When you change from small units to large units, you divide.**

- **When you change from large units to small units, you multiply.**

10 Handling data: collecting data

10.1 Collecting data

Teaching reference: (pp 106–115, sections 8.1–8.6)

- When designing questions to collect data for a questionnaire
  (a) be clear what you want to find out, and what data you need
  (b) ask short simple questions
  (c) avoid questions which are too vague, too personal or which may influence the answer.

- When you carry out a survey select a random sample to avoid bias.

- When you collect data from experiments use a data capture sheet, for example

Colour of hair	Tally
Blonde	|||
Brown	卌	
Ginger	||
Grey	||||

卌 = 5 people

Example 1

The weights in kilograms of 30 people are recorded:

```
67  42  58  62  71  92  38  67  61  52
68  44  61  65  43  55  69  80  71  66
54  73  77  88  66  60  55  61  93  42
```

Design a data capture sheet on which this data can be collected.
Record the above data on the data capture sheet.

Our data capture sheet will be a tally chart with weights in units of 10 kg.

Weight (w) in kg	Tally	Frequency
$0 \leqslant w < 10$		
$10 \leqslant w < 20$		
$20 \leqslant w < 30$		
$30 \leqslant w < 40$			1
$40 \leqslant w < 50$	||||	4
$50 \leqslant w < 60$	卌	5
$60 \leqslant w < 70$	卌 卌 ||	12
$70 \leqslant w < 80$	||||	4
$80 \leqslant w < 90$	||	2
$90 \leqslant w < 100$	||	2

The tallies and frequencies have been completed on the sheet.

Example 2

Tony wishes to conduct a survey into the TV viewing habits of people.
In his questionnaire he asks the question

'You enjoy watching soap operas, don't you?'

(a) Explain why this is not a good question to ask.
(b) Write three suitable questions which invite people to provide
reasonable information about soap operas.

(a) The question is a poor one because it is leading; it invites a
person to answer YES.
(b) Three suitable questions might be:

1. Tick the box which most accurately gives the number of
hours (t) you spend each week watching soap operas on TV:

Do not watch	$0 < t \leqslant 1$	$1 < t \leqslant 2$	$2 < t \leqslant 3$	$3 < t \leqslant 4$	$4 < t \leqslant 5$	More than 5
☐	☐	☐	☐	☐	☐	☐

2. From the following list of soap operas, write the numbers 1,
2 and 3 in the boxes for your three favourites.

Neighbours	☐	Home and Away	☐
Coronation Street	☐	Crossroads	☐
Brookside	☐	Other	☐
Eastenders	☐		

3. If you have written a 1, 2 or 3 in the box next to 'Other' in
question 2, please write the name of this other soap opera
on the line below:

Other is _____

Example 3

This table is an extract from a motorcar dealership's advertisement:

Price	Make	Age	Registration	Mileage
£9500	Vauxhall	2	V	12 000
£8999	Ford	1	X	9 000
£6995	Rover	3	R	19 000
£5495	Nissan	4	R	32 000
£4995	Vauxhall	4	P	49 000
£3995	Saab	7	L	63 000
£3995	Ford	5	N	51 000
£2500	Peugeot	7	M	39 000
£1995	Seat	8	K	78 000
£1495	Vauxhall	9	J	98 000

(a) Write down the make of the car that has a price of £5495.
(b) Write down the price and registration of the car that has done
the least mileage.
(c) Write down the makes of the two cars aged 7.

(a) Look down the price column until you get to £5495 and see

  £5495 Nissan

so the make is a Nissan.

(b) Look down the mileage column: the least mileage is 9000, so looking across you see

  £8999 Ford 1 X 9000

The price is £8999 and the registration is X.

(c) Look down the age list:

  £3995 Saab   7
  £2500 Peugeot 7

The two makes aged 7 are Saab and Peugeot.

Exercise 10A   Links (*10A–10F*) 8A–8G

1 A set of 30 weights in kg is recorded:

  13.1 8.7 6.8 4.3 5.6 18.1 8.3 14.0 10.8 21.7
  22.2 6.0 13.6 3.1 11.5 10.8 15.7 3.7 9.4 8.0
   6.4 17.0 7.3 12.8 13.5 12.9 10.0 4.2 16.0 11.5

Complete the frequency table below, using intervals of 5 seconds.

Weight (w) in kg	Tally	Frequency
$0 \leqslant w < 5$		

2 Shani and Erica were carrying out a survey on the sweets people eat in the office canteen.

Shani wrote the question 'Which sweets do you eat?'
Erica said that this question was too vague.

Write down two ways in which the question could be improved.

3 Billy's home is near a busy main road. He decides to carry out a survey of the different types of car that travel on the main road.

Design a suitable data capture sheet so that he can collect the data easily.

4   30 people used an off-licence one evening. They bought:

Beer   Wine   Spirits   Wine   Sherry   Wine
Sherry   Sherry   Sherry   Beer   Sherry   Beer
Beer   Beer   Spirits   Spirits   Beer   Spirits
Beer   Beer   Beer   Sherry   Sherry   Spirits
Beer   Beer   Sherry   Spirits   Beer   Sherry

Complete the table to show this information:

Drink	Tally	Frequency
Beer		
Wine		
Spirits		
Sherry		

Total   30

5   Alex and June were collecting information on the type of music bought by students in their school.

Draw a suitable data collection sheet for this information.

6   Jack decides to conduct a survey about shopping habits. To conduct his survey he stands in the High Street at 11 am and asks the people who pass by a number of questions.

Explain why this technique will lead to biased results.

7   The table below is an extract from a travel company's advertisement for summer holidays:

Place	Month	Duration	Method of Travel	Cost
Austria	August	14 days	Coach	£365
Majorca	August	7 days	Fly	£399
Tenerife	July	14 days	Fly	£650
Costa Brava	June	7 days	Coach	£199
Paris	June	3 days	Rail	£159
Barcelona	July	3 days	Fly	£269
Sorrento	July	14 days	Fly	£599
Minorca	June	14 days	Fly	£450
Capri	August	7 days	Fly	£859
Edinburgh	July	4 days	Rail	£249

(a) Write down the cost of a 14 day holiday to Sorrento in July.
(b) Peter can afford to spend a maximum of £300 on his holiday. Write down the names of all the places from the above list he can afford to visit.
(c) Where are the two places you could go to by coach?
(d) Amy must take her holiday in August. She can only take a maximum of seven days and can afford no more than £500. Write down the name of the only place she can visit from the above list.

8   The table opposite shows the
     names of six students and the
     marks they received in some
     recent modular tests.
     (a) Who had the highest mark
           in Mathematics?
     (b) Who had the lowest mark in
           Science?
     The pass mark in English was 56.
     (c) Who **did not** pass English?

	English	Science	Mathematics
Gary	52	61	48
Fiona	73	34	69
Asif	55	73	67
Sumreen	57	68	83
Jane	81	66	72
Philip	56	39	47

9   The mid-day temperatures, in degrees Celsius, were recorded
     one day for 40 different towns. The results were:

     18.6   19.3   21.2   17.8   18.3   18.4   22.8   19.6   18.8   17.2
     16.3   17.0   21.4   18.0   16.2   19.1   22.2   18.4   17.9   15.4
     15.8   22.5   20.8   21.7   18.9   18.5   17.6   18.3   20.1   20.0
     17.6   22.0   21.4   19.3   18.0   16.6   20.1   19.2   20.2   18.3

     (a) Design a data capture sheet on which these temperatures
           could be recorded in intervals of 1 degree, starting at 1°C.
     (b) Complete your data capture sheet for the above temperatures.

10   Jack is designing a survey to find out about people who use a
     chip shop near his home. One of the things he wants to find
     out is how far people have travelled to get to the chip shop.
     (a) Decide which question below is best to ask. Give two
           reasons for your decision.
             A How far have you travelled to get here today?
             B Where do you live?
             C Do you live far from here?
             D Please show me on the map where you have travelled from.
     Jack decides to do the survey one Friday evening outside the chip shop.
     (b) Give one reason why this would give a biased sample.

Summary of key points

■   **When designing questions to collect data for a questionnaire**
    (a) be clear what you want to find out, and what data you need
    (b) ask short simple questions
    (c) avoid questions which are too vague, too personal or
          which may influence the answer.

■   **Select a random sample to avoid bias.**

■   **When you collect data from experiments use a data**
    capture sheet, for example

Colour of hair	Tally
Blonde	|||
Brown	Ⱨﾞ |
Ginger	||
Grey	||||

‖‖‖ = 5 people

11 Handling data: representing and interpreting data

11.1 Tally charts, bar charts, pictograms and pie charts

Teaching reference:
(*pp 133–135, section 10.1;*
pp 139–142, section 10.4;
pp 201–208, sections 16.1,
16.2, 16.3
pp 159–161, section 10.1
pp 163–165, section 10.3

■ A tally chart can be used to display data that can be counted.

■ A bar chart can be used to display data that can be counted.

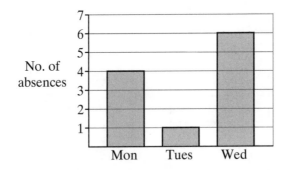

■ A pictogram can be used to illustrate data that can be counted using symbols to represent amounts.

Jan	🧍 🧍 🧍
Feb	🧍 🧍
Mar	🧍 🧍 🧍
Apr	

🧍 = 100 people

■ Pie charts are usually used to display data that can be counted.
The angles at the centre of a pie chart add up to 360°.
The sections of the pie chart are a useful way of seeing the relative proportions.

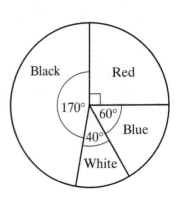

Example 1

Joanne conducted a survey of the 30 students in her class.
She asked each student to name their favourite colour.
The results of this survey are shown below:

Blue   Red   Red   Green   Black   Red   Yellow   Blue   Red   Pink
Red   Red   Blue   Black   White   Red   Yellow   Green   Red   White
Red   Blue   Yellow   White   Red   Blue   Green   Yellow   White   Red

(a) Represent these results on a tally chart.

Favourite colour	Tally	Frequency
Blue		
Red		
Green		
Black		
Yellow		
Pink		
White		

(b) Draw a bar chart to show this information.

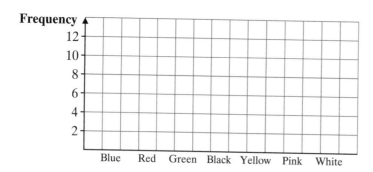

(c) Which is the most common favourite colour for the students in Joanne's class?

(a)

Favourite colour	Tally	Frequency
Blue	ⅢⅢ	5
Red	ⅢⅢ ⅢⅢ Ⅰ	11
Green	ⅠⅠⅠ	3
Black	ⅠⅠ	2
Yellow	ⅠⅠⅠⅠ	4
Pink	Ⅰ	1
White	ⅠⅠⅠⅠ	4

(b) **Frequency**

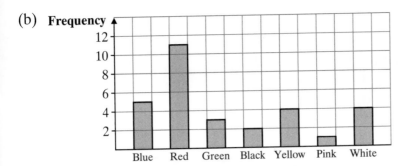

(c) Either the tally chart or the bar chart tells us that the most common favourite colour is the one with the greatest frequency, so it is red.

Example 2

Here is a pictogram showing the number of drivers caught speeding in Askhorne last week.

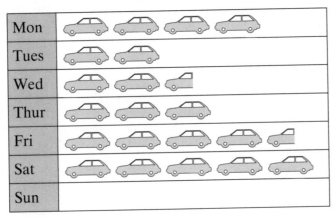

= 20 drivers

(a) Write down the number of drivers caught speeding in Askhorne
   (i)   last Monday
   (ii) last Wednesday
   (iii) last Friday.

Last Sunday 30 drivers were caught speeding.
(b) Show this on the pictogram.

(a) (i)   80
    (ii) 50
    (iii) 90

(b) | Sun |

Example 3

There are 30 students in a class.
The table provides information about the ways these students usually travel to school each day:

Method	Frequency
Walk	10
Bus	5
Cycle	3
Private car	8
Taxi	4

Draw a pie chart for this information.
On the pie chart, the angle for Walk will be

$\frac{10}{30} \times 360 = 120°$

The other angles are

Bus: $\frac{5}{30} \times 360 = 60°$ Cycle: $\frac{3}{30} \times 360 = 36°$

Private car: $\frac{8}{30} \times 360 = 96°$ Taxi: $\frac{4}{30} \times 360 = 48°$

So the pie chart is

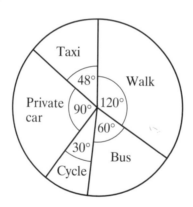

Exercise 11A   **Links (10A, 10D, 16A, 16B) 10A**

1   Forty people were asked to name the make of car they drove.
Their answers are given below:

Ford	Skoda	Ford	Vauxhall	Jaguar	BMW	Vauxhall	Ford
BMW	Rover	Vauxhall	Ford	Rover	Fiat	Ford	Fiat
Rover	Ford	Ford	Vauxhall	Ford	Jaguar	Vauxhall	Ford
Ford	Vauxhall	Rover	Ford	BMW	Fiat	Honda	Honda
Rover	Ford	Ford	Honda	Ford	Jaguar	Ford	Ford

(a) Complete a tally chart for this information.
(b) Draw a bar chart for this information.

(c) For these forty people, which is the most popular make of car they drive?

(d) Draw a pie chart to represent all of this information.

2 The pictogram shows the number of swimmers who used the swimming pool on four days last week.

Sun	![swimmer]![swimmer]![swimmer]
Mon	![swimmer]![swimmer]![swimmer]![swimmer]
Tues	![swimmer]![swimmer]
Wed	

![swimmer] = 10 swimmers

(a) How many swimmers used the swimming pool last Sunday?

(b) How many swimmers used the pool last Monday?

On Wednesday 35 swimmers used the swimming pool.

(c) Show this information on the pictogram.

3 Harry collected data on the food some people bought in the restaurant today. Here are his results:

Food	Frequency
Pizza	5
Curry	12
Fish and chips	10
Eggs and bacon	3

(a) On a grid draw a bar chart to show this information.

(b) Show the information on a pie chart.

4 **Sixty** people used a sports centre one evening.
They each took part in only one of the following activities:

Aerobics Badminton Football Squash Tennis

Information about the activities in which they took part is shown in this pie chart:

(a) Which of the activities was most popular?

(b) How many of the 60 people took part in aerobics?

(c) What fraction of the 60 people took part in football?

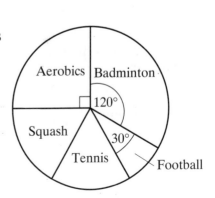

11.2 Measures of average and spread

Teaching reference:
(*pp 251–266, sections 20.1–20.4*)
pp 161–163, section 10.2
pp 308–322, sections 20.1–20.6

- The **mode** of a set of data is the value which occurs most times.

- The **median** is the middle value when the data is arranged in order of size.

- The **mean** of a set of data is the sum of the values divided by the number of these values.

$$\text{mean} = \frac{\text{sum of values}}{\text{number of values}}$$

- The **range** of a set of data is the difference between the highest and the lowest value:

$$\text{range} = \text{highest value} - \text{lowest value}$$

- The **modal class** is the group which has the greatest frequency.

Example 4

Zara did 10 Science homeworks last term.

Her marks were 3, 2, 8, 7, 7, 4, 9, 4, 7, 5.

(a) Write down the mode of these marks.
(b) Find the median of these marks.
(c) Work out the mean of these marks.
(d) Work out the range of these marks.

(a) We can see that the number 7 is the one that occurs most often, so the mode is 7.

(b) Write the numbers in order as

$$2, 3, 4, 4, 5, 7, 7, 7, 8, 9$$

The median is the number in the middle of this row. But because there are 10 (an even number) values there are two numbers in the middle; these are 5 and 7. The median is then

$$\frac{5+7}{2} = \frac{12}{2} = 6$$

So the median is 6.

(c) The mean of the marks is

$$\frac{3+2+8+7+7+9+4+7+5}{10} = \frac{56}{10} = 5.6$$

So the mean is 5.6.

(d) The range is the highest number minus the lowest number, so the range is

$$9 - 2 = 7$$

i.e. the range is 7.

Example 5

Forty people took part in a competition.

The points scored are grouped in the frequency table below:

Points scored	Frequency
1 to 5	2
6 to 10	4
11 to 15	8
16 to 20	10
21 to 25	13
26 to 30	3

Write down the modal class interval.

The modal class interval is the class interval with the highest frequency.

So the modal class interval is 21 to 25.

Exercise 11B	**Links (20A to 20F) 10B**

1   Asif had 5 bags of potatoes.
   The numbers of potatoes in each bag were 30, 28, 31, 27, 28.
   (a) Work out the mean number of potatoes per bag.
   (b) Work out the range of the number of potatoes.

2   Last term Jenny did 10 homeworks in History.
   Her marks were

   7, 6, 8, 4, 5, 5, 9, 8, 8, 4

   (a) Find the mode of these marks.
   (b) Find the median of these marks.
   (c) Work out the mean mark.
   (d) Work out the range of these marks.

3   In a spelling test 11 students scored these marks:

   11, 20, 14, 19, 10, 7, 11, 17, 12, 16, 9

   (a) Work out the median.
   (b) Work out the range.

4   Sixty students took a Science test.
   The maximum number of marks on the test was 50.
   The table shows information about the marks obtained
   by the students.
   Write down the modal class for this information.

Marks	Frequency
1 to 10	4
11 to 20	16
21 to 30	17
31 to 40	20
41 to 50	3

11.3 Interpretation and implications

■ **Diagrams and graphs can be interpreted.**

■ **Data and findings will usually have implications.**

Example 6

The diagram shows the average mid-day temperature in London and Malta during the summer months:

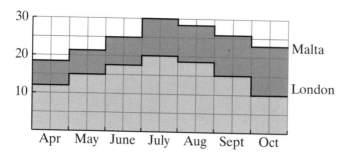

(a) During which of these months is the average mid-day temperature in London at its highest?
(b) During which of these months is the difference between average mid-day temperatures in Malta and London at its greatest?

(a) Looking at the graph, the average mid-day temperature in London is at its highest in July. So the answer is July.
(b) The difference between the two temperatures is measured by the gap between the two bold lines. This gap is at its greatest during the month of October, so the answer is October.

Example 7

There are 15 girls and 15 boys in class 11T.
During registration they did a spelling test with a maximum mark of 20.

The median mark for the girls was 16, with a range of 4.
The median mark for the boys was 12, with a range of 10.

By comparing the results explain whether the girls or the boys did better in the spelling test.

By just comparing the medians it looks as if the girls, on the whole, did better than the boys.
However, taking the ranges into account and given a maximum mark of 20 it could be possible that several boys scored a mark higher than the maximum mark for the girls.
So the evidence is inconclusive about whether the girls or the boys did better.

Exercise 11C   Links (*10C, 10E*) 10C

1   The graph shows information about the average number of
    hours of sunshine per day in London and Tenerife during the
    summer months.

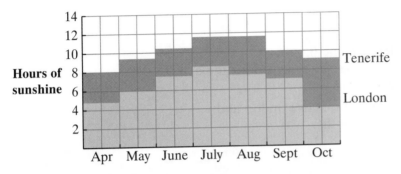

(a) During which of these months does Tenerife have the
     highest average number of hours of sunshine?
(b) During which of these months is the difference between
     the average number of hours of sunshine in Tenerife and
     in London at its least?

2   Mrs Rogers gave her class a mental arithmetic test.
    The median mark for the boys was 7 and the range of the
    marks for the boys was 4.
    The median mark for the girls was 6 and the range of the
    marks for the girls was 8.
    Explain whether the boys or the girls did better in this mental
    arithmetic test.

Exercise 11D   Mixed questions

1   Forty people were asked to name their favourite type of music.
    The results of this enquiry are given below:

Pop	Classical	Jazz	Rock	Pop	Jazz	Pop	Rock	Pop	Pop
Jazz	Rock	Rock	Pop	Pop	Rock	Jazz	Pop	Pop	Rock
Rock	Classical	Pop	Pop	Jazz	Jazz	Rock	Pop	Rock	Pop
Pop	Classical	Pop	Rock	Rock	Pop	Pop	Pop	Jazz	Rock

(a) Complete the tally chart and frequency table:

Type of music	Tally	Frequency

(b) Draw a bar chart to show this information.
(c) Draw a pie chart for this information.

2 Here is a list of the marks Sally received for her ten homeworks in Geography:

7, 4, 8, 9, 9, 6, 9, 7, 5, 4

(a) Write down the mode of these marks.
(b) Work out the median of the marks.
(c) Work out the mean mark.
(d) Work out the range of the marks.

Sally did one more homework.
The range of her marks then became 6.

(e) What were the possible marks she received for the extra homework? Give your reasons.

3 The bar charts show the temperatures in London and Barcelona during the summer months:

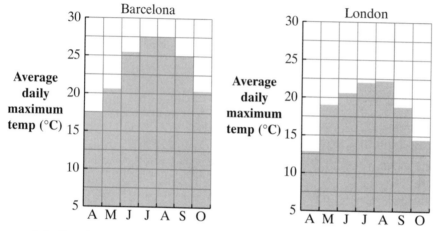

(a) During which month is the temperature at its highest in London?
(b) Work out the difference between temperatures in London and Barcelona during May.

4 The table gives some information about the favourite subjects of 90 students:

Subject	Frequency	Angle
English	36	
History	18	
Art		
Maths		
Total	90	

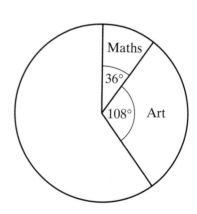

(a) Use the information in the table to complete the pie chart.
(b) Use the information in the pie chart to complete the table.
(c) Which of these four subjects is
 (i) most popular   (ii) least popular?

5   Dominique did a survey of the shoe sizes of 72 students at her
school. The results of the survey are shown below:

```
7  4  5   6  7  4  3  5  5  7  8   5   3  6  6   6  4  5
4  5  8   9  5  6  6  5  6  7  6   5   4  4  5   6  6  6
5  3  9  11  6  7  8  6  6  8  4   9  10  8  6  10  7  7
7  4  4  10  9  7  8  6  5  4  3  11  10  9  6   5  6  5
```

(a) Draw a tally chart and frequency table for this data.
(b) Represent the data on a bar chart.
(c) Represent the data on a pie chart.
(d) What is the mode of the shoe sizes?

Dominique's friend did a survey of shoe sizes in another
school. She told Dominique that at the other school the mode
of the shoe sizes was 7.

(e) Explain whether or not there is sufficient evidence to
suggest that the students at the other school have, in
general, larger feet than the students at Dominique's school.

Summary of key points

■   **A tally chart can be used to display data that can be
counted.**

■   **A bar chart can be used to display data that can be
counted.**

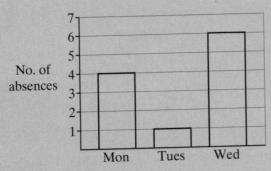

■   **A pictogram can be used to illustrate data that can be
counted using symbols to represent amounts.**

- Pie charts are usually used to display data that can be counted.
  The angles at the centre of a pie chart add up to 360°.
  The sections of the pie chart are a useful way of seeing the relative proportions.

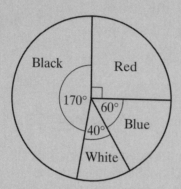

- The mode of a set of data is the value which occurs most times.

- The median is the middle value when the data is arranged in order of size.

- The mean of a set of data is the sum of the values divided by the number of these values:

$$\text{mean} = \frac{\text{sum of values}}{\text{number of values}}$$

- The range of a set of data is the difference between the highest and the lowest value:

  range = highest value − lowest value

- The modal class is the group which has the greatest frequency.

- Diagrams and graphs can be interpreted.

- Data and findings will usually have implications.

12 Probability

Probability is used to predict the chance of things, called **events**, happening in the future.

12.1 The probability scale

Teaching reference: pp 355–360, sections 23.1, 23.2, 23.3

- The likelihood of something happening can be placed on a likelihood scale from *impossible* to *certain*.

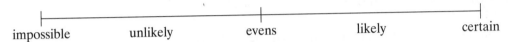

impossible   unlikely   evens   likely   certain

- Probability is measured on a scale of 0 to 1. You must write a probability as a fraction, decimal or percentage.

0 $\frac{1}{4}$ $\frac{1}{2}$ $\frac{3}{4}$ 1

- An event, such as *tossing a coin*, can have different *outcomes*, such as landing Heads or Tails.

- When one outcome prevents another outcome from happening the outcomes are *mutually exclusive*.
  (When you toss a coin the events Heads and Tails are mutually exclusive.)

- The expression '*are equally likely*' means '*have an equal chance*'.

- When an outcome is *impossible* it has *no chance* and its probability $= 0$.

- When an outcome is *certain* its probability $= 1$.

- When an event has exactly *two outcomes* each of which is *equally likely* then the *probability of each outcome is $\frac{1}{2}$*.

Example 1

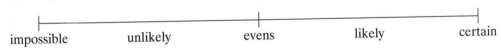

impossible   unlikely   evens   likely   certain

On the likelihood scale above, mark each of the following:

(a) it will snow in London on 1st August (use the letter A)
(b) the day before Christmas Day will be Christmas Eve (use the letter B)
(c) the bottom card of a well shuffled pack of cards will be coloured black (use the letter C)
(d) there will be at least one rainy day during March (use the letter D)

(e) ice cream will not melt if you put it in a hot oven for half an hour (use the letter E).

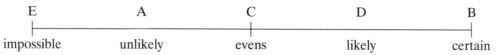

Example 2

On the probability scale below, mark the following probabilities:

(a) The next baby to be born will be female (use the letter F)
(b) The day immediately following Christmas Day will be Boxing Day (use the letter B)
(c) The next thing you see flying in the sky will be a pink elephant (use the letter E)
(d) The top card on a well shuffled pack of cards will be a Heart (use the letter H).

(a) We know that about half of new born babies are boys and about half are girls. So the probability of the baby being a girl is about $\frac{1}{2}$ (see key points).

So the position of F should be

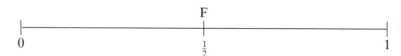

(b) It is a certainty that Christmas Day will be followed by Boxing Day, so (see key points) the probability $= 1$.
So the position of B should be

(c) We can say that elephants cannot fly and neither are they pink. So it is impossible for you to see a flying pink elephant. So (see key points) this probability $= 0$.
So the position of E should be

(d) The top card in a well shuffled pack can be a Club, Diamond, Heart or Spade, and these outcomes each have the same chance. There are 4 outcomes with equal chances, so (see key points) the probability of the top card being a Heart is $\frac{1}{4}$.

So the position of H should be

Exercise 12A   **Links (23A) 23A**

---

1   On the likelihood scale below:
   (a) mark with T the likelihood of a fair coin landing Tails
        when it is tossed once
   (b) mark with C the likelihood of the day before Boxing Day
        being Christmas Day
   (c) mark with S the likelihood of the Sun shining in London
        on at least one day next July
   (d) mark with D the likelihood that a dinosaur will walk down
        the main road tomorrow
   (e) mark with J the likelihood that Mr Jones will cut his lawn
        at a time when it is pouring down with rain.

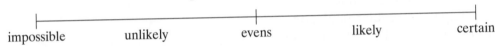

2   On the probability line below:
   (a) mark with T the probability of getting a Tail when a fair
        coin is thrown
   (b) mark with S the probability of getting a 9 when a fair
        six-sided dice is thrown
   (c) mark with N the probability of getting a number less than
        100 when a fair six-sided dice is thrown.

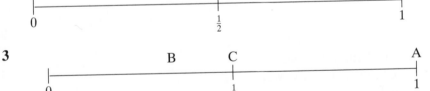

Three letters are marked on the scale.
Match the letters to these probabilities:
The probability that a fair six-sided dice will land with its top
face showing a number less than 3.   Letter __
The probability that the Sun will set tomorrow.   Letter __
The probability that when it is tossed once a fair coin will land
Tails.   Letter __

4   On the probability line below, mark the following probabilities:
   (a) it will snow in Manchester in July (use the letter M)
   (b) the Sun will set tomorrow (use the letter S)

(c) a fair coin when tossed will come down Tails (use the letter T)

(d) a fair dice when rolled will show a four (use the letter F).

12.2 Mutually exclusive outcomes

■ **When an event has *n* mutually exclusive and equally likely outcomes the probability of any one of the outcomes happening is $\frac{1}{n}$.**

■ **When there are *n* mutually exclusive outcomes and *a* successful outcomes the probability of a successful outcome is $\frac{a}{n}$.**

Example 3

The diagram represents a five-sided spinner.
The spinner is in the shape of a regular pentagon.
Each section of the spinner is labelled with a letter.

The spinner is to be spun once.

Write down the probability that it will land on

(a) the section labelled B

(b) a section labelled A

(c) a section labelled E

(d) a section labelled with a letter of the alphabet

(e) a section labelled with a letter that is **not** a vowel

(f) a section labelled either A or B.

See the key points:

(a) The spinner could land on any one of 5 sections. But of these only 1 is labelled B. So the probability of it landing on this section is $\frac{1}{5}$.

(b) There are again 5 sections but 2 of them are labelled A, so the probability of it landing on A is $\frac{2}{5}$.

(c) There are no sections labelled E, so landing on one is impossible. Therefore this probability $= 0$.

(d) Each and every section is labelled with a letter. So it is a certainty that the spinner must land on a section labelled with a letter. So this probability $= 1$.

(e) The vowels are A, E, I, O and U. So B, C and D are **not** vowels. So the probability of landing on a section with a letter that is not a vowel is $\frac{3}{5}$.

(f) There are 2 sections labelled A and 1 section labelled B. So there are 3 sections altogether labelled A or B. So the probability of landing on a section labelled either A or B is $\frac{2+1}{5} = \frac{3}{5}$.

Exercise 12B   Links (*23B, 23C*) 23B, 23C

1 Joan has three equal-sized coloured balls in a bag.
One ball is red, one ball is blue and the other ball is green.
She chooses a ball at random.
   (a) Write down the probability that the ball she chooses will be blue.
   (b) Write down the probability that the ball she chooses will be yellow.

2 An ordinary six-sided dice has each of its faces labelled with one of the numbers from 1 to 6.
The dice is rolled once.
Write down the probability of its upper face
   (a) showing 4
   (b) showing a number greater than 3
   (c) showing an even number
   (d) showing a number between 7 and 10.

3 Farouk has a bag of 15 chocolates.
8 are plain, 6 are milk and 1 is white.
He chooses a chocolate at random.
   (a) Which type of chocolate is it most likely to be? Give your reason.
   (b) Write down the probability of the chosen chocolate being white.
   (c) Write down the probability of Farouk choosing a fruit gum.
   (d) Write down the probability of the chosen chocolate being milk.
   (e) Write down the probability of the chosen chocolate being either plain or white.

4 The diagram represents a six-sided fair spinner.
The spinner is in the shape of a regular hexagon.
The sections of the spinner are labelled with the letters A, B, C, D and E.
The spinner is to be spun once.
   (a) Write down the probability that it will land on D.
   (b) Write down the probability that it will land on A.
   (c) Write down the probability that it will land on a vowel.
   (d) Write down the probability that it will land on P.

5   Asif has a bag of 10 equal-sized coloured balls.
Six of the balls are red, three of the balls are blue, and one of
the balls is white.
A ball is to be selected at random.
Write down the probability that the selected ball
(a) will be white
(b) will be blue
(c) will be either blue or white
(d) will be yellow.

6   The diagram represents a fair spinner.
The spinner is in the shape of a regular hexagon.
The sections of the spinner are labelled with letters.
The spinner is to be spun once.
Write down the probability that it will land on
(a) a section marked A
(b) a section marked B
(c) a section marked C
(d) a section marked D.

7   Here is a spinner.

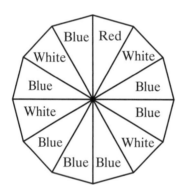

The spinner is spun once.
(a) (i) On which of the colours is it most likely to land?
(ii) Give a reason for your answer.
(b) On the probability line, mark with an X the probability
that the colour it lands on will be red.

(c) Write down the probability that the colour it lands on will
be white.

12.3 Listing outcomes

■ **Outcomes of a single event, or two successive events, can be
listed in a systematic way.**

Teaching reference:
(pp 299–302, sections 23.6,
23.7)
pp 363–369, sections 23.6,
23.7

Example 4

Take a square-shaped spinner as shown right.
Each section of the spinner is labelled with a number.

Take also a coin.
The faces of the coin are Heads and Tails.

The spinner is to be spun once.
The coin is to be tossed once.

One possible joint outcome of the two events is

(1, Heads)

(a) List all possible joint outcomes of the two events.
(b) Explain why the probability of the spinner landing on 1 and
the coin landing Heads is $\frac{1}{8}$.

(a) (See key point) It is important to be systematic. So we work as

(1, Heads) then (1, Tails)
(2, Heads) then (2, Tails)
(3, Heads) then (3, Tails)
(4, Heads) then (4, Tails)

(b) There are 8 possible outcomes as listed above.
Each of these outcomes is equally likely.
The outcome (1, Heads) is one of these outcomes.
So the probability of this outcome is $\frac{1}{8}$.

Exercise 12C   Links *(23F, 23G)* **23F, 23G**

1   Tom has four places to visit. These are

London, Manchester, Bristol and Edinburgh

In each case he has three possible methods of travelling:

Car, bus or train

One possible journey he could make is

London by train

List all the possible journeys Tom could make.

2   Here is a spinner:

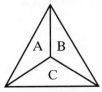

Here is a normal six-sided dice:

The spinner is to be spun once and the dice rolled once.

The joint outcome of the section the spinner lands on and the number on the top face of the dice is to be recorded. One such outcome could be

(A, 1)

(a) Make a list of all possible joint outcomes.
(b) Write down the probability of getting the joint outcome (A, 1).
(c) Write down the probability of getting the joint outcome (D, 3).

3   A game is played with two fair spinners. The spinners are spun at the same time.
The diagram below shows the result (Red, 3).

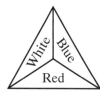 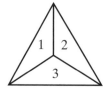

(a) List all the possible results when the spinners are spun once.
(b) Use your list to work out the probability of getting (Blue, 1) when the spinners are spun once.

4   Kylie has a fair coin and a fair six-sided dice.
She tosses the coin once.
She rolls the dice once.

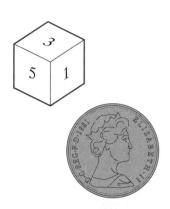

The diagram shows the outcome (Heads, 3).
(a) List all the possible outcomes when the coin is tossed once and the dice is rolled once.
(b) Use your list to work out the probability of getting the result (Tails, 6) when the coin is tossed once and the dice is rolled once.

Summary of key points

■ **The likelihood of something happening can be placed on a likelihood scale from *impossible* to *certain*.**

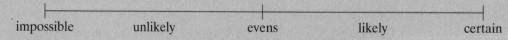

impossible   unlikely   evens   likely   certain

■ **Probability is measured on a scale of 0 to 1. You must write a probability as a fraction, decimal or percentage.**

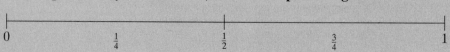

0 $\frac{1}{4}$ $\frac{1}{2}$ $\frac{3}{4}$ 1

■ **An event, such as *tossing a coin*, can have different *outcomes*, such as landing Heads or Tails.**

■ When one outcome prevents another outcome from happening the outcomes are *mutually exclusive*. (When you toss a coin the events Heads and Tails are mutually exclusive.)

■ The expression '*are equally likely*' means '*have an equal chance*'.

■ When an outcome is *impossible* it has *no chance* and its probability $= 0$.

■ When an outcome is *certain* its probability $= 1$.

■ When an event has exactly *two outcomes* each of which is *equally likely* then the *probability of each outcome is* $\frac{1}{2}$.

■ When an event has n mutually exclusive and equally likely outcomes the probability of any one of the outcomes happening is $\frac{1}{n}$.

■ When there are n mutually exclusive outcomes and a successful outcomes the probability of a successful outcome is $\frac{a}{n}$.

■ Outcomes of a single event, or two successive events, can be listed in a systematic way.

Examination style practice paper

Section 1 You must not use a calculator.

1 (a) Write the number twenty thousand and two using figures. (1)

(b) Write 12 852 to the nearest hundred. (1)

(c) Write these numbers in order of size. Start with the smallest number.

9495   9594   9954   9549   9459   9945 (2)

2

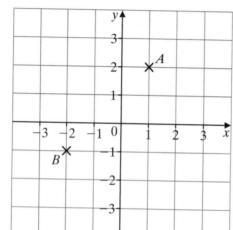

(a) Write down the coordinates of the points (i) *A*, (ii) *B*. (2)

(b) (i) Measure the length of the line *AB* in millimetres.

(ii) Express your answer to part (i) in centimetres. (2)

3 (a) Write 22.8 correct to the nearest integer. (1)

(b) Work out 22.8×10. (1)

(c) Work out $22.8 \div 4$. (1)

4

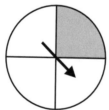

The diagram shows a fair spinner.
Hayley spins the pointer.
The pointer stops on either grey or white.

(a) On the probability scale, mark with a cross the probability that the pointer will stop on grey. Label it G. (1)

(b) On the probability scale, mark with a cross the probability that the pointer will stop on white. Label it W. (1)

5 **(a)** Work out $\frac{5}{6} \times 42$.   (1)

    (b) Find the simplest form of $\frac{25}{45}$.   (1)

6

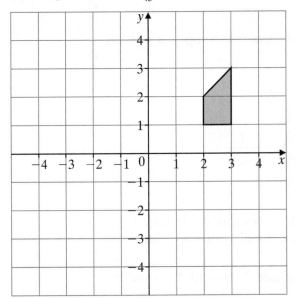

    (a) Write down the mathematical name of the shaded quadrilateral.   (1)

    (b) Rotate the shaded quadrilateral a half-turn about the origin.   (3)

Section 2 You may use a calculator.

1 Write down

    (a) a multiple of 4,   (1)

    (b) a factor of 77,   (1)

    (c) two common factors of 24 and 42.   (2)

2

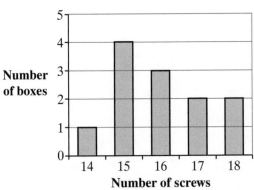

Barry bought some boxes of screws.
He counted the number of screws in each box.
The bar chart shows his results.

    (a) How many boxes contained 17 screws?   (1)

    (b) Write down the modal number of screws.   (1)

    (c) How many boxes of screws did Barry buy?   (1)

    (d) Work out the range of the number of screws. (1)

3   A biro costs 12 pence.
    (a) Write down an expression for the cost, in pence, of b biros. (1)
    (b) Simplify $4y - 2y + 7y - 3y$. (1)
    (c) Multiply $7c \times 3d$. Give your answer as simply as possible. (1)
    (d) Expand $4(3x + 5)$. (1)

4

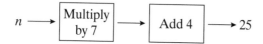

    (a) How many lines of symmetry does this shape have? (1)
    (b) Write down the order of rotational symmetry of the shape. (1)

5   Write 0.45, 4% and $\frac{2}{5}$ in order of size. Start with the smallest. (3)

6   Here are two number machines.

$$n \longrightarrow \boxed{\begin{array}{c}\text{Multiply}\\\text{by 7}\end{array}} \longrightarrow \boxed{\text{Add 4}} \longrightarrow 25$$

The input number is n and the output number is 25.
Write down an equation for n. (2)